10169

QA
276
S4

D1264482

THE LINEAR HYPOTHESIS: A GENERAL THEORY

G. A. F. SEBER

M. Sc. (New Zealand), Ph. D. (Manchester), F. S. S.
Lecturer in Mathematics, University of Auckland
New Zealand

BEING NUMBER NINETEEN OF
GRIFFIN'S STATISTICAL
MONOGRAPHS & COURSES
EDITED BY
M. G. KENDALL, M.A., Sc. D.

1966
HAFNER PUBLISHING COMPANY
NEW YORK

Copyright © 1966
CHARLES GRIFFIN & COMPANY LIMITED
42 DRURY LANE, LONDON, W.C.2

First published . . . 1966

PRINTED IN GREAT BRITAIN BY
LATIMER TREND & CO LTD, WHITSTABLE

PREFACE

During the past ten years numerous books have been written on the subject of linear hypotheses under the guise of regression analysis, analysis of variance, and experimental design. As these books vary considerably in approach, notation, and mathematical difficulty, the mathematically minded reader who wishes to understand some of the basic ideas behind the subject with a minimum attention to detail may find it hard to know where to start. It is mainly for such a reader that this book has been written.

The approach given here, namely that of developing linear hypothesis theory in a vector space framework, is not only a very general one, but is also much simpler and more readily capable of geometrical interpretation. For this reason I feel that the mathematically oriented reader will find this viewpoint more satisfying.

Although this approach is well known among theoretical statisticians and is taught in some universities, the literature using this method is scattered and to my knowledge has not been collected together before for publication. I hope that this book fills such a gap, and that it may perhaps stimulate more university lecturers to teach the subject in this way.

With regard to the content of the book, a basic knowledge of matrix theory and vector spaces is assumed known, though most of the results needed are summarised in Chapter 1. In Chapter 2 the linear hypothesis is defined, and Chapters 3 and 4 deal with the estimation of unknown parameters and tests of linear hypotheses using the F statistic. The properties of power and robustness of the F test are summarised briefly in Chapter 5. The problem of testing several hypotheses is considered in Chapter 6 and the concept of orthogonality is discussed in detail with reference to complete layouts in analysis of variance, experimental designs such as randomised blocks and Latin squares, and regression analysis. Chapter 7, entitled "Modified Hypotheses", deals with the method of analysis of covariance as applied to both experimental design and regression analysis. In Chapter 8 the question of "missing" observations is considered and various applications are given. Up till now only univariate hypotheses have been considered, and Chapter 9 is devoted to extending some of the previous theory to multivariate hypotheses. This chapter is rather sketchy as I am not concerned with multivariate analysis in general, but just with one or two basic principles. The material in Chapter 10, on non-linear regression, is based

D. HIDEN RAMSEY LIBRARY
U. N. C. AT ASHEVILLE
ASHEVILLE, N. C.

mainly on papers published in the last couple of years, and this chapter is likely to undergo some modification in the future. Chapter 11 deals with large sample theory applied to non-linear hypotheses and, at the expense of boring some readers, I have tried to be as rigorous as possible with the minimum of detail. Two brief Appendices, followed by a list of the references mentioned in the text, complete the book.

In a book of this size, where the emphasis is on compactness, one is bound to miss out some important topics in a subject which covers so many fields. Therefore a "selection" rule was needed, and to some extent this has been biased by my own interests and research. However, I have endeavoured to include those topics which most readily fit into the vector space framework; other specialised topics such as the rejection of outliers or dubious observations have been omitted, important though they may be. To compensate for this, I have endeavoured to give sufficient references to these other topics to assist the interested reader in finding the relevant literature. These references are given not only in the text but also at the end of many of the chapters, together with a brief comment on their subject-matter. It is possible, of course, that some of these topics may eventually be incorporated into the vector space framework.

In conclusion I would like to express my debt to Dr S. D. Silvey of Manchester University for first introducing me to this vector space approach. His course on linear hypothesis theory, together with many helpful discussions, provided a foundation for the early chapters of this book, which was written while the author held an assistant lectureship in Statistics at the London School of Economics. I would also like to thank Messrs M. Knott and K. Ord for reading the manuscript and for their valuable criticisms and suggestions.

Finally my thanks go to Miss Marion Knight who so patiently typed the difficult manuscript.

London,
August 1965

G. A. F. SEBER

CONTENTS

D. HIDEN RAMSEY LIBRARY
U. N. C. AT ASHEVILLE
ASHEVILLE, N. C.

CHAPTER 1

PRELIMINARIES

1.1 Notation

Matrices and vectors are denoted by bold-faced letters such as **A**, **a**, and scalars or constants by ordinary small letters. The $n \times n$ matrix with diagonal elements $\lambda_1, \lambda_2, \ldots, \lambda_n$ and zeros elsewhere is denoted by $\text{diag}(\lambda_1, \lambda_2, \ldots, \lambda_n)$ and when all the λ_i's are unity we have the identity matrix $\mathbf{I}_n$. The n-dimensional vector with all its elements equal to unity is denoted by $\mathbf{1}_n$.

Much of the notation from set theory will be incorporated in the text, e.g. $\in$, $\subset$ and $\cap$ represent "belongs to", "is contained in", and "intersection of" respectively.

If $\mathbf{x}$ is an n-dimensional column vector with elements $x_1, x_2, \ldots, x_n$ then the *length* of $\mathbf{x}$ is denoted by $\|\mathbf{x}\|$. Thus

$$\|\mathbf{x}\| = \sqrt{(\mathbf{x}'\mathbf{x})} = \sqrt{(x_1^2 + x_2^2 + \ldots + x_n^2)}.$$

We say that two vectors $\mathbf{x}$ and $\mathbf{y}$ are orthogonal, i.e. $\mathbf{x} \perp \mathbf{y}$, if $\mathbf{x}'\mathbf{y} = 0$.

If the $n \times n$ matrix $\mathbf{A}$ has elements a_{ij} we write $\mathbf{A} = [(a_{ij})]$. The *trace* of $\mathbf{A}$, which we denote by $\text{tr}[\mathbf{A}]$, is $\sum_{i=1}^{n} a_{ii}$.

Finally we would mention the "dot" and "bar" notation representing summation and averaging respectively; thus $x_{\cdot} = \sum_{i=1}^{n} x_i$ and $\bar{x}_{\cdot} = x_{\cdot}/n$.

A certain amount of linear algebra will be assumed known by the reader, and for a short revision course the author recommends a study of Appendices I and II of Scheffé (1959).

1.2 The linear vector space

The concept of a linear vector space is fundamental to the study of linear hypotheses and may be defined as follows: a *linear vector space* is a set of vectors V such that for any two vectors $\mathbf{x}$ and $\mathbf{y}$ belonging to V and for any real numbers a and b the vector $a\mathbf{x} + b\mathbf{y}$ also belongs to V. Although this definition is not the most general

D. HIDEN RAMSEY LIBRARY
U. N. C. AT ASHEVILLE
ASHEVILLE, N. C.

one that can be given (cf. Birkhoff and MacLane, 1953), it is sufficient for the development given in this book. From now on we shall drop the word "linear" and take it as understood. Usually all the vectors in V are n-dimensional vectors and therefore belong to n-dimensional Euclidean space which we denote by E_n.

If V is a vector space, then $V^{\perp}$, the set of all vectors in E_n perpendicular to V (called the *orthogonal complement* of V), is also a vector space. This follows from the fact that if $\mathbf{v} \in V$ and $\mathbf{x}$ and $\mathbf{y}$ belong to $V^{\perp}$, then

$$\mathbf{v}'(a\mathbf{x} + b\mathbf{y}) = a\mathbf{v}'\mathbf{x} + b\mathbf{v}'\mathbf{y} = 0 \quad \text{and} \quad a\mathbf{x} + b\mathbf{y} \in V^{\perp}.$$

If $\mathbf{X}$ is an $n \times r$ matrix and $R[\mathbf{X}]$ is the set of all vectors $\boldsymbol{\theta}$ such that $\boldsymbol{\theta} = \mathbf{X}\boldsymbol{\beta}$ for some $\boldsymbol{\beta}$, that is $R[\mathbf{X}] = \{\boldsymbol{\theta} : \boldsymbol{\theta} = \mathbf{X}\boldsymbol{\beta}\}$, then $R[\mathbf{X}]$ is a vector space. Also if $N[\mathbf{X}] = \{\boldsymbol{\phi} : \mathbf{X}\boldsymbol{\phi} = \mathbf{0}\}$ then $N[\mathbf{X}]$ is also a vector space. Thus to every matrix $\mathbf{X}$ there correspond two fundamental vector spaces known as the *range space*, $R[\mathbf{X}]$, and the *null space*, $N[\mathbf{X}]$, of $\mathbf{X}$. These spaces are related by the following lemma.

Lemma 1.2.1. $N[\mathbf{X}] = \{R[\mathbf{X}']\}^{\perp}$. In words this states that the orthogonal complement of the range space of $\mathbf{X}$ transposed is the null space of $\mathbf{X}$.

Proof. If $\boldsymbol{\theta} \in N[\mathbf{X}]$ then $\mathbf{X}\boldsymbol{\theta} = \mathbf{0}$ and $\boldsymbol{\theta}$ is orthogonal to each row of $\mathbf{X}$. Thus $\boldsymbol{\theta}$ is orthogonal to any linear combination of the rows of $\mathbf{X}$ and therefore $\boldsymbol{\theta} \perp R[\mathbf{X}']$. Conversely if $\boldsymbol{\theta} \perp R[\mathbf{X}']$ then $\mathbf{X}\boldsymbol{\theta} = \mathbf{0}$ and $\boldsymbol{\theta} \in N[\mathbf{X}]$. This completes the proof.

1.3 Basis of a vector space

A set of vectors $\boldsymbol{\beta}_1, \boldsymbol{\beta}_2, \ldots, \boldsymbol{\beta}_p$ is said to *span* a vector space V if every vector $\mathbf{v} \in V$ can be expressed as a linear combination of these vectors, that is, if there exist constants $b_1, b_2, \ldots b_p$ such that

$$\mathbf{v} = \sum_{i=1}^{p} b_i \boldsymbol{\beta}_i.$$

The vectors $\boldsymbol{\beta}_1, \boldsymbol{\beta}_2, \ldots, \boldsymbol{\beta}_p$ are *linearly independent* if $\sum_{i=1}^{p} b_i \boldsymbol{\beta}_i = \mathbf{0}$ implies that $b_1 = b_2 = \ldots = b_p = 0$. Thus linear independence implies that there is no non-trivial linear relation among the vectors. If the vectors $\boldsymbol{\beta}_1, \ldots, \boldsymbol{\beta}_p$ span V and are linearly independent then they are said to form a *basis* of V. Although a basis is not unique, the number of vectors p in it is unique and is called the *dimension* of V or $\dim[V]$. From every basis of V it is possible to construct an *orthonormal basis* $\boldsymbol{\alpha}_1, \boldsymbol{\alpha}_2, \ldots, \boldsymbol{\alpha}_p$ such that $\boldsymbol{\alpha}_i'\boldsymbol{\alpha}_j = \delta_{ij}$; "ortho" as the vectors are mutually orthogonal and "normal" as they have unit length. It is always possible to enlarge such an orthonormal basis to the set $\boldsymbol{\alpha}_1, \boldsymbol{\alpha}_2, \ldots, \boldsymbol{\alpha}_p, \boldsymbol{\alpha}_{p+1}, \ldots, \boldsymbol{\alpha}_n$ to form an orthonormal basis for E_n. Thus if $\dim[V] = p$, then $\boldsymbol{\alpha}_{p+1}, \ldots, \boldsymbol{\alpha}_n$ form a basis for $V^{\perp}$ and $\dim[V^{\perp}] = n-p$.

Since the range space $R[\mathbf{X}]$ of a matrix $\mathbf{X}$ is the space spanned by its columns, then $\dim[R[\mathbf{X}]]$ will be the number of linearly independent columns of $\mathbf{X}$ and therefore the rank of $\mathbf{X}$. The dimension of $N[\mathbf{X}]$ is known as the nullity of $\mathbf{X}$ and is obtained from the rule

$$\text{rank} + \text{nullity} = \text{number of columns of } \mathbf{X}.$$

Thus if $\mathbf{X}$ is an $n \times r$ matrix of rank p, then $\dim[R[\mathbf{X}]] = p$ and $\dim[N[\mathbf{X}]] = r-p$.

1.4 Addition and intersection of vector spaces

A vector space V is said to be the *direct sum* of two vector spaces V_1 and V_2 if every vector $\mathbf{v} \in V$ can be expressed *uniquely* in the form $\mathbf{v} = \mathbf{v}_1 + \mathbf{v}_2$ where $\mathbf{v}_i \in V_i$ $(i = 1, 2)$. We represent this symbolically by $V = V_1 \oplus V_2$. If we drop the word unique from the definition we say that V is the *sum* of V_1 and V_2 and write $V = V_1 + V_2$.

The intersection of two vector spaces V_1 and V_2 is denoted by $V_1 \cap V_2$ and is the set of all vectors which belong to both spaces.

EXERCISES (1) If V_1 and V_2 are vector spaces, prove that $V_1 \oplus V_2$, $V_1 + V_2$ and $V_1 \cap V_2$ are also vector spaces.

(2) Show that for every vector space V there exists a matrix $\mathbf{C}$ such that $V = N[\mathbf{C}]$.

The following lemma will be useful later on.

Lemma 1.4.1. If V_1 and V_2 are two vector spaces then

$$[V_1 \cap V_2]^{\perp} = V_1^{\perp} + V_2^{\perp}.$$

Proof. Let $\mathbf{C}_1$ and $\mathbf{C}_2$ be matrices such that $V_i = N[\mathbf{C}_i]$ for $i = 1, 2$. Then

$$[V_1 \cap V_2]^{\perp} = \left\{N\begin{bmatrix}\mathbf{C}_1\\ \mathbf{C}_2\end{bmatrix}\right\}^{\perp}$$

$$= R[(\mathbf{C}_1', \mathbf{C}_2')] \quad \text{(cf. lemma 1.2.1)}$$

D. HIDEN RAMSEY LIBRARY
U. N. C. AT ASHEVILLE
ASHEVILLE, N. C.

$$= R[\mathbf{C}_1'] + R[\mathbf{C}_2']$$
$$= V_1^{\perp} + V_2^{\perp}.$$

1.5 Idempotent matrices

The symbol **P** will always represent a symmetric idempotent matrix, i.e. $\mathbf{P}' = \mathbf{P}$ and $\mathbf{PP} = \mathbf{P}$.

Lemma 1.5.1. The eigen values of a symmetric idempotent matrix **P** are zero or one, and the number of unit eigen values is the rank of **P**.

Proof. Suppose **P** is $n \times n$. As **P** is symmetrical there exists an $n \times n$ orthogonal matrix **S** such that

$$\mathbf{S}'\mathbf{PS} = \text{diag}(\lambda_1, \lambda_2, \ldots, \lambda_n) = \mathbf{\Lambda} \text{ say,}$$

where $\lambda_1, \lambda_2, \ldots, \lambda_n$ are the eigen values of **P**. Now

$$\mathbf{\Lambda}^2 = \mathbf{S}'\mathbf{PSS}'\mathbf{PS} = \mathbf{S}'\mathbf{PPS}' = \mathbf{S}'\mathbf{PS} = \mathbf{\Lambda}$$

and $\lambda_i^2 = \lambda_i$. Thus the only possible eigen values are zero or one, and the rank of **P**, which is the number of non-zero eigen values, is therefore the number of unit eigen values.

EXERCISE 3. Prove that $\mathbf{I}-\mathbf{P}$ is also idempotent, and hence show that $\mathbf{y}'(\mathbf{I}-\mathbf{P})\mathbf{y} \geqslant 0$.

1.6 Lagrange multipliers

For the reader who is not familiar with the use of Lagrange multipliers we include a brief section on their use. Suppose we wish to minimise a function $h(\theta_1, \theta_2, \ldots, \theta_n)$ subject to k independent linear constraints $\mathbf{a}_i'\boldsymbol{\theta} = 0\,(i = 1, 2, \ldots, k)$. Then we introduce an unknown constant called a Lagrange multiplier μ_i for each constraint and minimise the function $h(\boldsymbol{\theta}) + \sum_i \mu_i(\mathbf{a}_i'\boldsymbol{\theta})$. The relative minimum, $\boldsymbol{\theta}_0$, is then given by

$$\partial h(\boldsymbol{\theta}_0)/\partial\theta_j + \sum_i \mu_i a_{ij} = 0 \quad (j = 1, 2, \ldots, n)$$

and

$$\mathbf{a}_i'\boldsymbol{\theta}_0 = 0 \quad (i = 1, 2, \ldots, k),$$

where a_{ij} is the jth element of $\mathbf{a}_i$. We thus have $(k+n)$ equations in $(k+n)$ unknowns $\boldsymbol{\theta}_0$ and $\boldsymbol{\mu}$, and therefore – theoretically – they can be solved. If we put $\mathbf{A}' = [\mathbf{a}_1, \mathbf{a}_2, \ldots, \mathbf{a}_k] = [(a_{ji})]$ and let $\mathbf{h}_0$ be the vector with jth element $\partial h(\boldsymbol{\theta}_0)/\partial\theta_j$, then the equations can be written in the form

$$\mathbf{h}_0 + \mathbf{A}'\boldsymbol{\mu} = \mathbf{0}$$

and

$$\mathbf{A}\boldsymbol{\theta}_0 = \mathbf{0}.$$

1.7 The multivariate normal distribution

Let $y_1, y_2, \ldots, y_n$ be random variables with means $\theta_1, \theta_2, \ldots, \theta_n$ and let $D[\mathbf{y}]$ represent the $n \times n$ matrix with i,jth element $E[(y_i-\theta_i)(y_j-\theta_j)]$, $E[.]$ denoting expectation with respect to the variable in brackets. This is known as the dispersion matrix of $\mathbf{y}$ and can be written in the form

$$D[\mathbf{y}] = E[(\mathbf{y}-\boldsymbol{\theta})(\mathbf{y}-\boldsymbol{\theta})'] = \mathbf{D}, \text{ say.}$$

If $\mathbf{y}$ is distributed as the multivariate normal distribution with mean vector $\boldsymbol{\theta}$ and dispersion matrix $\mathbf{D}$, we write $\mathbf{y}$ is $\mathcal{N}[\boldsymbol{\theta}, \mathbf{D}]$ and the likelihood function of $\mathbf{y}$ is $(2\pi)^{-n/2}|\mathbf{D}|^{-\frac{1}{2}} \exp\{-\frac{1}{2}(\mathbf{y}-\boldsymbol{\theta})'\mathbf{D}^{-1}(\mathbf{y}-\boldsymbol{\theta})\}$. In most of this book $\mathbf{D} = \sigma^2\mathbf{I}_n$, where σ^2 is an unknown constant. The matrix $\mathbf{D}$ takes this form when the variables y_i are uncorrelated (and therefore independent when normally distributed) and have the same variance σ^2.

EXERCISE 4. If $\mathbf{y}$ is $\mathcal{N}[\boldsymbol{\theta}, \sigma^2 I_n]$ and $\mathbf{y} = \mathbf{T}\mathbf{z}$, where $\mathbf{T}$ is an orthogonal matrix, then $\mathbf{z}$ is $\mathcal{N}[\mathbf{T}'\boldsymbol{\theta}, \sigma^2\mathbf{I}_n]$.

1.8 The non-central chi-squared distribution

Suppose $\mathbf{y}$ is $\mathcal{N}[\boldsymbol{\theta}, \sigma^2\mathbf{I}_n]$, then the characteristic function $M_j(t)$ for y_j^2/σ^2 is

$$M_j(t) = \int_{-\infty}^{\infty} (2\pi\sigma^2)^{-\frac{1}{2}} \exp\{-(y_j-\theta_j)^2/2\sigma^2 + ity_j^2/\sigma^2\}\, dy_j$$

$$= \int_{-\infty}^{\infty} (2\pi\sigma^2)^{-\frac{1}{2}} \exp\{-[y_j - \theta_j/(1-2it)]^2(1-2it)/2\sigma^2\}\, dy_j \times$$

$$\times \exp\{\theta_j^2/2\sigma^2(1-2it) - \theta_j^2/2\sigma^2\}$$

$$= (1-2it)^{-\frac{1}{2}} \exp\{-\theta_j^2/2\sigma^2 + \theta_j^2/2\sigma^2(1-2it)\}. \qquad (1.8.1)$$

Since the variables $y_1, y_2, \ldots, y_n$ are independent, the characteristic function of $z = \sum_{j=1}^{n} y_j^2/\sigma^2$ is $\phi_n(t, \delta)$, where

$$\phi_n(t,\delta) = \prod_{j=1}^{n} M_j(t)$$

$$= (1-2it)^{-n/2} \exp\{-\delta/2 + \delta/2(1-2it)\}$$

and

$$\delta = \sum_{j=1}^{n} \theta_j^2/\sigma^2.$$

D. HIDEN RAMSEY LIBRARY
U. N. C. AT ASHEVILLE
ASHEVILLE, N. C.

The variable z is said to have the non-central chi-squared distribution with n degrees of freedom and non-centrality parameter δ; the distribution is usually denoted by $\chi^2_{n,\delta}$. When each θ_i is zero, $\delta = 0$ and z has the (central) chi-squared distribution χ^2_n with characteristic function

$$\phi_n(t, 0) = (1 - 2it)^{-n/2}.$$

Now

$$\phi_n(t, \delta) = e^{-\delta/2} \sum_{m=0}^{\infty} \frac{(\delta/2)^m}{m!} \phi_{n+2m}(t, 0),$$

and applying the inversion formula for characteristic functions termwise in the series, we obtain the density function $f_n(z, \delta)$, namely

$$f_n(z, \delta) = e^{-\delta/2} \sum_{m=0}^{\infty} \frac{(\delta/2)^m}{m!} f_{n+2m}(z, 0), \qquad (1.8.2)$$

where $f_{n+2m}(z,0)$ is the density function for χ^2_{n+2m}.

Thus $$f_n(z, \delta) = e^{-\delta/2} \sum_{m=0}^{\infty} \frac{(\delta/2)^m}{m!} \frac{z^{n/2+m-1} e^{-z/2}}{2^{n/2+m} \Gamma(n/2 + m)}$$

To find the mean of z, we note from the coefficient of it in the characteristic function of χ^2_n that $E[\chi^2_n] = n$. Hence

$$E[z] = e^{-\delta/2} \sum \frac{(\delta/2)^m}{m!} (n + 2m)$$

$$= n + \delta. \qquad (1.8.3)$$

Alternatively, $E[z]$ is the coefficient of it in $\log \phi_n(t,\delta)$, the cumulant-generating function of z.

EXERCISE 5. Show that the non-central chi-squared distribution has the same reproductive property as the central chi-squared, namely, that if two variables are distributed independently as $\chi^2_{n_1, \delta_1}$ and $\chi^2_{n_2, \delta_2}$, then the distribution of their sum is $\chi^2_{n_1+n_2, \delta_1+\delta_2}$.

1.9 Quadratic forms

If $\mathbf{y}$ is $\mathcal{N}[\boldsymbol{\theta}, \sigma^2\mathbf{I}_n]$ then we have the following fundamental lemmas.

Lemma 1.9.1. If $\mathbf{P}$ is symmetric and idempotent of rank r, then the quadratic $\mathbf{y}'\mathbf{P}\mathbf{y}/\sigma^2$ is distributed as non-central chi-squared with r degrees of freedom and non-centrality parameter $\boldsymbol{\theta}'\mathbf{P}\boldsymbol{\theta}/\sigma^2$.

Proof. If $\mathbf{P}$ is symmetric and idempotent, we may assume, without loss of generality, that the first r eigen values are unity and the rest zero (lemma 1.5.1). Then there exists an orthogonal matrix $\mathbf{S}$ such that

$$\mathbf{S}'\mathbf{P}\mathbf{S} = \begin{bmatrix} \mathbf{I}_r & 0 \\ 0 & 0 \end{bmatrix}.$$

Thus

$$\mathbf{P} = \mathbf{S}\begin{bmatrix} \mathbf{I}_r & 0 \\ 0 & 0 \end{bmatrix}\mathbf{S}'$$

$$= (\mathbf{s}_1, \mathbf{s}_2, \ldots, \mathbf{s}_r)\begin{pmatrix} \mathbf{s}_1' \\ \cdot \\ \cdot \\ \cdot \\ \mathbf{s}_r' \end{pmatrix}$$

$$= \mathbf{S}_r\mathbf{S}_r', \text{ say,}$$

where $\mathbf{s}_1, \mathbf{s}_2, \ldots, \mathbf{s}_r$ are the first r columns of $\mathbf{S}$. Putting $\mathbf{y} = \mathbf{S}\mathbf{z}$ gives

$$\mathbf{y}'\mathbf{P}\mathbf{y} = \mathbf{z}'\mathbf{S}'\mathbf{P}\mathbf{S}\mathbf{z}$$

$$= z_1^2 + z_2^2 + \cdots + z_r^2,$$

where $\mathbf{z}$ is $\mathcal{N}[\mathbf{S}'\boldsymbol{\theta}, \sigma^2\mathbf{I}_n]$, (by exercise 4, § 1.7).

Thus $\sum_{i=1}^{r} z_i^2/\sigma^2$ is $\chi^2_{r,\delta}$ where

$$\delta = \sum_{i=1}^{r} (\mathbf{s}_i'\boldsymbol{\theta})^2/\sigma^2$$

$$= \boldsymbol{\theta}'\mathbf{S}_r\mathbf{S}_r'\boldsymbol{\theta}/\sigma^2$$

$$= \boldsymbol{\theta}'\mathbf{P}\boldsymbol{\theta}/\sigma^2.$$

Corollary. The converse of this lemma is also true, that is, if $\mathbf{y}'\mathbf{A}\mathbf{y}/\sigma^2$ has a non-central chi-squared distribution, then $\mathbf{A}$ is symmetric and idempotent.

Proof. Let $\mathbf{y}'\mathbf{A}\mathbf{y}$ be any quadratic form and let $\mathbf{S}$ be the diagonalising orthogonal matrix. Putting $\mathbf{y} = \mathbf{S}\mathbf{z}$ gives

$$\mathbf{y}'\mathbf{A}\mathbf{y} = \lambda_1 z_1^2 + \lambda_2 z_2^2 + \ldots + \lambda_n z_n^2,$$

where $\lambda_1, \lambda_2, \ldots, \lambda_n$ are the eigen values of $\mathbf{A}$. From equation (1.8.1) the characteristic function of $\lambda_j z_j^2/\sigma^2$ is

$$N_j(t) = (1-2it\lambda_j)^{-\frac{1}{2}} \exp\{-(\mathbf{s}_j'\boldsymbol{\theta})^2[1/2\sigma^2 - 1/2\sigma^2(1-2it\lambda_j)]$$

and the characteristic function of $\mathbf{y}'\mathbf{A}\mathbf{y}/\sigma^2$ is then $\prod_{j=1}^{n} N_j(t)$. It is obvious that this can only take the form of $\phi_n(t,\delta)$ if each λ_j is zero or unity. Therefore if $\mathbf{y}'\mathbf{A}\mathbf{y}/\sigma^2$ has a non-central chi-squared distribution, the eigen values of $\mathbf{A}$ are zero or one, and from lemma 1.9.1 $\mathbf{A}$ can be expressed in the form $\mathbf{S}_r\mathbf{S}_r'$ where r is the rank of A. Thus

$$\mathbf{A}\mathbf{A} = \mathbf{S}_r(\mathbf{S}_r'\mathbf{S}_r)\mathbf{S}_r' = \mathbf{S}_r\mathbf{S}_r' = \mathbf{A}$$

and $\mathbf{A}$ is symmetric and idempotent. This completes the proof.

Lemma 1.9.2. If $\mathbf{A}_1$ and $\mathbf{A}_2$ are symmetric idempotent matrices such that $\mathbf{A}_1\mathbf{A}_2 = \mathbf{0}$, then $\mathbf{y}'\mathbf{A}_1\mathbf{y}$ and $\mathbf{y}'\mathbf{A}_2\mathbf{y}$ are statistically independent.

Proof.

$$\begin{aligned}\mathrm{cov}[\mathbf{A}_1\mathbf{y}, \mathbf{A}_2\mathbf{y}] &= E[\mathbf{A}_1\mathbf{e}\mathbf{e}'\mathbf{A}_2'] \\ &= \sigma^2\mathbf{A}_1\mathbf{A}_2' \\ &= \sigma^2\mathbf{A}_1\mathbf{A}_2 \\ &= \mathbf{0}.\end{aligned}$$

Therefore since $\mathbf{y}$ has a multivariate normal distribution, $\mathbf{A}_1\mathbf{y}$ and $\mathbf{A}_2\mathbf{y}$ are independent and the quadratic forms $\mathbf{y}'\mathbf{A}_i\mathbf{y} = (\mathbf{A}_i\mathbf{y})'\mathbf{A}_i\mathbf{y}$ $(i = 1,2)$ are independent.

1.10 The non-central F and Beta distributions

Suppose x_1 is $\chi^2_{r_1,\delta}$ and x_2 is $\chi^2_{r_2}$, then $F = \dfrac{r_2}{r_1}\dfrac{x_1}{x_2}$ is said to be distributed as the non-central F distribution with r_1, r_2 degrees of freedom and non-centrality parameter δ. It is usually denoted by $F_{r_1,r_2,\delta}$ and its derivation is similar to that of the ordinary (central) F distribution which we denote by F_{r_1,r_2}. If we denote the density function of F by $f_{r_1,r_2}(F;\delta)$ then by considering the distribution of x_1/x_2, it follows from equation (1.8.2) that

$$\begin{aligned}f_{r_1,r_2}(F;\delta) &= e^{-\delta/2}\sum_{m=0}^{\infty}\frac{(\delta/2)^m}{m!} f_{r_1+2m,r_2}(F;0) \\ &= e^{-\delta/2}\sum_{m=0}^{\infty}\frac{(\delta/2)^m}{m!}\left(\frac{r_1}{r_2}\right)^{r_1/2+m} F^{r_1/2-1+m} \times \\ &\quad\times\left(1+\frac{r_1}{r_2}F\right)^{-(r_1+r_2)/2-m}\{B[\tfrac{1}{2}r_1+m, \tfrac{1}{2}r_2]\}^{-1},\end{aligned}$$

where $B[a,b] = \Gamma(a)\Gamma(b)/\Gamma(a+b)$ and $f_{r_1+2m,r_2}(F;0)$ is the central $F_{r_1+2m,\, r_2}$ distribution.

Another statistic which is related to the F statistic is

$$v = \frac{x_1}{x_1 + x_2} = \frac{r_1 F}{r_1 F + r_2},$$

which is said to have the non-central Beta distribution. Performing the transformation we arrive at the density function

$$e^{-\delta/2} \sum_{m=0}^{\infty} \frac{(\delta/2)^m}{m!} \frac{v^{r_1/2+m-1}(1-v)^{r_2/2-1}}{B[\frac{1}{2}r_1+m, \frac{1}{2}r_2]}$$

1.11 Additional references

Linear algebra: Murdoch (1957), Hadley (1961).

Multivariate normal distribution: Anderson (1958).

For other derivations and properties of the non-central distributions cf. Tang (1938), Patnaik (1949), Johnson (1959), and Guenther (1964). Various approximations and alternative expressions for these distributions are given in Abdel-Aty (1954), Hodges (1955), Tukey (1957), Sankaran (1959), Pearson (1959), Hogben *et al.* (1961), Seber (1963), Price (1964), and Amos (1964).

A general discussion on quadratic forms in normal variables is given in Kendall and Stuart (1958), Plackett (1960a) and Graybill (1961). Further references are Solomon (1960), Imhop (1961), and Ruben (1963).

For the independence of non-homogeneous quadratic forms, cf. Good (1963).

CHAPTER 2

THE LINEAR HYPOTHESIS

2.1 Regression analysis

Our first example of a linear hypothesis is found in regression analysis. Suppose we have a random variable y with mean θ and we assume that θ is a linear function of p fixed variables $x_0, x_1, \ldots, x_{p-1}$, namely, $\theta = \beta_0 x_0 + \cdots + \beta_{p-1} x_{p-1}$ where the β's are unknown constants. For n values of the x's, we get n observations on y, giving the model G

$$\begin{aligned} y_i &= \theta_i + e_i, \\ &= x_{i0}\beta_0 + x_{i1}\beta_1 + \cdots + x_{i,p-1}\beta_{p-1} + e_i \end{aligned}$$

for $i = 1, 2, \ldots, n$, where $E[e_i] = 0$. This is known as a multiple linear regression in p variables, and by putting $x_{ij} = x_i^j$ we see that the polynomial regression model

$$y_i = \beta_0 + \beta_1 x_i + \beta_2 x_i^2 + \cdots + \beta_{p-1} x_i^{p-1} + e_i,$$

of degree $p-1$ for a single variable x, is included as a special case.

Two assumptions about the errors e_i are generally made: (i) the errors are uncorrelated, or $\mathrm{cov}(e_i, e_j) = 0$ for $i \neq j$, and (ii) the errors have the same variance σ^2. We are usually interested in testing the hypothesis H that $\beta_q = \beta_{q+1} = \cdots = \beta_{p-1} = 0$, and to do this we add a further assumption that the errors are normally distributed. If we define $\mathbf{X} = [(x_{ij})]$, $\boldsymbol{\beta}' = (\beta_0, \beta_1, \ldots, \beta_{p-1})$ and let $\mathbf{X}_q$ represent the matrix consisting of the first q columns of $\mathbf{X}$, then the model, assumptions and hypothesis can be written in the form $\mathbf{y} = \boldsymbol{\theta} + \mathbf{e}$ where $\mathbf{e}$ is $\mathscr{N}[\mathbf{0}, \sigma^2 \mathbf{I}_n]$, $G : \boldsymbol{\theta} = \mathbf{X}\boldsymbol{\beta}$ and $H : \boldsymbol{\theta} = \mathbf{X}_q \boldsymbol{\beta}_q$, where $\boldsymbol{\beta}_q$ is the first q elements of $\boldsymbol{\beta}$. In this situation, $\mathbf{X}$ usually has full rank, that is the rank of $\mathbf{X}$ is p. If we define $\Omega = R[\mathbf{X}]$ and $\omega = R[\mathbf{X}_q]$ then from §1.2 we have that Ω and ω are both vector spaces. Thus H is the linear hypothesis that $\boldsymbol{\theta}$ belongs to a vector space ω, given the assumption G that it belongs to a vector space Ω.

2.2 Analysis of variance

Other examples of linear hypotheses are found in analysis of variance models, and we consider as an example the hypothesis H that the means of two populations are equal. Suppose we have t observations y_{ij}, $j = 1, 2, \ldots, t$, on the ith population with mean θ_i $(i = 1, 2)$. Then we consider the model $y_{ij} = \theta_{ij} + e_{ij}$, where the e_{ij} are once again the error terms, and $\theta_{ij} = \theta_i$ for $j = 1, 2, \ldots, t$. If we express the elements y_{ij}, θ_{ij} and e_{ij} as elements in single $2t$-dimensional vectors, for example $\boldsymbol{\theta}' = (\theta_{11}, \theta_{12}, \ldots, \theta_{1t}, \theta_{21}, \ldots, \theta_{2t})$, the model becomes $\mathbf{y} = \boldsymbol{\theta} + \mathbf{e}$ as in the regression example above. Putting $\mu = \bar{\theta}_{.}$ and $\alpha_i = \theta_i - \bar{\theta}_{.}$, we can write $G : \boldsymbol{\theta} = \mathbf{X}\boldsymbol{\beta}$ where $\boldsymbol{\beta}' = (\mu, \alpha_1, \alpha_2)$. The matrix $\mathbf{X}$ is given by

$$\mathbf{X}' = \begin{bmatrix} \overbrace{1 \ldots 1}^{t} & \overbrace{1 \ldots 1}^{t} \\ 1 \ldots 1 & 0 \ldots 0 \\ 0 \ldots 0 & 1 \ldots 1 \end{bmatrix}$$

and is not of full rank since the first row is the sum of the other two. However, the parameters μ, α_1 and α_2 are uniquely defined as $\alpha_1 + \alpha_2 = 0$, and this condition is necessary and sufficient for the identifiability of these parameters (see later in §3.4). The hypothesis H becomes $\alpha_1 = \alpha_2 = 0$ or $\boldsymbol{\theta} = \mathbf{1}_{2t}\mu$; thus once again, as in §2.1, we have $\Omega = R[\mathbf{X}]$ and $\omega = R[\mathbf{X}_1]$.

However, in this example we can reformulate the hypothesis in such a way as to dispense with the need of introducing identifiability constraints. Since $\theta_{ij} = \bar{\theta}_{i.} = \theta_i$ then

$$\theta_{ij} - \bar{\theta}_{i.} = 0 \quad \text{for } i = 1, 2;\ j = 1, 2, \ldots, t. \tag{2.2.1}$$

This is equivalent to $\mathbf{A}\boldsymbol{\theta} = \mathbf{0}$ where $\mathbf{A}$ is the $2(t-1) \times 2t$ matrix corresponding to the $2(t-1)$ independent constraints on the θ_{ij} given by equation (2.2.1). In a similar manner H is equivalent to $\mathbf{C}\boldsymbol{\theta} = 0$ where $\mathbf{C}' = (\mathbf{A}', \mathbf{A}_1')$, $\mathbf{A}_1$ being the $1 \times 2t$ matrix corresponding to the equation $\bar{\theta}_{1.} - \bar{\theta}_{2.} = 2(\bar{\theta}_{1.} - \bar{\theta}_{..}) = 0$. Here we use the double dot notation; thus $\bar{\theta}_{..} = \sum_i \sum_j \theta_{ij}/2t$. We note that $\mathbf{A}$ is only a $1 \times 2t$ matrix since $\alpha_1 + \alpha_2 = 0$ and the two constraints $\alpha_i = \bar{\theta}_{i.} - \bar{\theta}_{..} = 0$ $(i = 1, 2)$ are therefore not independent. Thus we have the null space representation $\Omega = N[\mathbf{A}]$ and $\omega = N[\mathbf{C}]$.

2.3 General definition

The above examples illustrate what we mean by a linear hypothesis, and we now give a formal definition. Let $\mathbf{y} = \boldsymbol{\theta} + \mathbf{e}$, where $\boldsymbol{\theta}$ is known to belong to a vector space Ω, then a linear hypothesis H is a hypothesis which states that $\boldsymbol{\theta} \in \omega$ a linear subspace of Ω. The assumption that $\boldsymbol{\theta} \in \Omega$ we denote by G.

For purposes of estimation we add the assumptions $E[\mathbf{e}] = \mathbf{0}$ and $D[\mathbf{e}] = \sigma^2 \mathbf{I}_n$, and for testing H we add the further assumption that $\mathbf{e}$ has the multivariate normal distribution.

Some non-linear hypotheses can be converted to linear ones by a suitable transformation. For example, suppose $\boldsymbol{\theta} = \mathbf{X}\boldsymbol{\beta}$, where $\mathbf{X}$ has full rank, and we wish to test $H : \mathbf{A}\boldsymbol{\beta} = \mathbf{a}$, where $\mathbf{A}$ and $\mathbf{a}$ are known and $\mathbf{a} \neq \mathbf{0}$. Then according to our general definition, H is not a linear hypothesis as $\omega = \{\boldsymbol{\theta} : \mathbf{A}(\mathbf{X}'\mathbf{X})^{-1}\mathbf{X}'\boldsymbol{\theta} = \mathbf{a}\}$ is not a linear vector space. However, if we choose any vector $\mathbf{c}$ such that $\mathbf{A}\mathbf{c} = \mathbf{a}$ and put

$$\mathbf{z} = \mathbf{y} - \mathbf{X}\mathbf{c}, \quad \boldsymbol{\phi} = \boldsymbol{\theta} - \mathbf{X}\mathbf{c}, \quad \boldsymbol{\gamma} = \boldsymbol{\beta} - \mathbf{c},$$

we have

$$\mathbf{z} = \boldsymbol{\phi} + \mathbf{e}, \quad G : \boldsymbol{\phi} = \mathbf{X}\boldsymbol{\gamma}$$

and $H : \mathbf{A}\boldsymbol{\gamma} = \mathbf{A}(\mathbf{X}'\mathbf{X})^{-1}\mathbf{X}'\boldsymbol{\phi} = \mathbf{0}$ is now a linear hypothesis.

In some examples the underlying model takes the form $\mathbf{y} = \boldsymbol{\theta} + \boldsymbol{\eta}$, where $\boldsymbol{\eta}$ is $\mathscr{N}[\mathbf{0}, \sigma^2\mathbf{B}]$ and $\mathbf{B}$ is a known positive definite matrix. Since $\mathbf{B}$ is positive definite, there exists a non-singular matrix $\mathbf{V}$ such that $\mathbf{B} = \mathbf{V}\mathbf{V}'$ (Appendix I, lemma 1), and the transformation $\mathbf{z} = \mathbf{V}^{-1}\mathbf{y}$, $\boldsymbol{\phi} = \mathbf{V}^{-1}\boldsymbol{\theta}$ transforms the model to $\mathbf{z} = \boldsymbol{\phi} + \mathbf{e}$, where

$$D[\mathbf{e}] = E[\mathbf{e}\mathbf{e}'] = \sigma^2\mathbf{V}^{-1}(\mathbf{V}\mathbf{V}')(\mathbf{V}')^{-1} = \sigma^2\mathbf{I}_n$$

as before. To see that linear hypotheses remain linear we note that

$$\begin{aligned}\Omega &= \{\boldsymbol{\theta} : \boldsymbol{\theta} = \mathbf{Y}\boldsymbol{\beta}\} \\ &= \{\boldsymbol{\phi} : \boldsymbol{\phi} = \mathbf{V}^{-1}\mathbf{Y}\boldsymbol{\beta}\}\end{aligned}$$

where the columns of $\mathbf{Y}$ are any basis of Ω.

When the sample size is large, many non-linear non-normal models can be approximated by linear ones, and in Chapter 11 we describe this approximation.

CHAPTER 3

LEAST SQUARES ESTIMATION

3.1 Principle of least squares

Suppose we have the model $\mathbf{y} = \boldsymbol{\theta} + \mathbf{e}$, where $E[\mathbf{e}] = \mathbf{0}$, $D[\mathbf{e}] = \sigma^2 \mathbf{I}_n$, and $\boldsymbol{\theta} \in \Omega$, a p-dimensional vector space. A reasonable estimate for $\boldsymbol{\theta}$ would be the value $\boldsymbol{\theta}_0$ which minimises the total error sum of squares $e_1^2 + e_2^2 + \ldots + e_n^2 = \|\mathbf{e}\|^2$, that is, which minimises $\|\mathbf{y} - \boldsymbol{\theta}\|^2$ subject to $\boldsymbol{\theta} \in \Omega$. A clue as to how we might calculate $\boldsymbol{\theta}_0$ is given by considering the simple case in which $\mathbf{y}$ is a point P in three dimensions and Ω is a plane through the origin O. We have to find the point Q $(= \boldsymbol{\theta}_0)$ in the plane so that PQ^2 is a minimum; this is obviously the case when OQ is the orthogonal projection of OP on the plane. This idea can now be generalised into the following theorem.

Theorem 3.1.1. The least squares estimate $\boldsymbol{\theta}_0$ which minimises $\|\mathbf{y}-\boldsymbol{\theta}\|^2$ for $\boldsymbol{\theta} \in \Omega$ is the orthogonal projection of $\mathbf{y}$ on Ω.

Proof. Let $\boldsymbol{\alpha}_1, \boldsymbol{\alpha}_2, \ldots, \boldsymbol{\alpha}_p$ be an orthonormal basis for Ω and let $c_i = \mathbf{y}'\boldsymbol{\alpha}_i$. Then

$$\begin{aligned} \mathbf{y} &= \sum_{i=1}^{p} c_i \boldsymbol{\alpha}_i + (\mathbf{y} - \sum_{i=1}^{p} c_i \boldsymbol{\alpha}_i) \\ &= \mathbf{a} + \mathbf{b}, \text{ say.} \end{aligned}$$

Now

$$\begin{aligned} \boldsymbol{\alpha}_j'\mathbf{b} &= \boldsymbol{\alpha}_j'\mathbf{y} - \sum_i c_i \boldsymbol{\alpha}_j'\boldsymbol{\alpha}_i \\ &= c_j - \sum_i c_i \delta_{ij} \\ &= 0. \end{aligned}$$

Thus $\mathbf{a} \in \Omega$, $\mathbf{b} \perp \Omega$ and we have decomposed $\mathbf{y}$ into two orthogonal vectors. This decomposition is unique, for if not, there will exist some other decomposition $\mathbf{y} = \mathbf{a}_1 + \mathbf{b}_1$. Then $\mathbf{a}_1 - \mathbf{a} = \mathbf{b}_1 - \mathbf{b}$ and since $\mathbf{a}_1 - \mathbf{a} \in \Omega$ and $\mathbf{b}_1 - \mathbf{b} \in \Omega^{\perp}$, both these vectors must be the zero vector; therefore $\mathbf{a}_1 = \mathbf{a}$ and $\mathbf{b}_1 = \mathbf{b}$. The unique vector $\mathbf{a}$ is the orthogonal projection of $\mathbf{y}$ on Ω and we now show that $\mathbf{a} = \boldsymbol{\theta}_0$. Since

$$(\mathbf{y} - \mathbf{a})'(\mathbf{a} - \boldsymbol{\theta}) = \mathbf{b}'(\mathbf{a} - \boldsymbol{\theta}) = 0,$$

we have from $\mathbf{y} - \boldsymbol{\theta} = (\mathbf{y} - \mathbf{a}) + (\mathbf{a} - \boldsymbol{\theta})$ the relation

$$\begin{aligned} \|\mathbf{y} - \boldsymbol{\theta}\|^2 &= \|\mathbf{y} - \mathbf{a}\|^2 + \|\mathbf{a} - \boldsymbol{\theta}\|^2 + 2(\mathbf{y} - \mathbf{a})'(\mathbf{a} - \boldsymbol{\theta}) \\ &= \|\mathbf{y} - \mathbf{a}\|^2 + \|\mathbf{a} - \boldsymbol{\theta}\|^2. \end{aligned}$$

Thus $\|\mathbf{y} - \boldsymbol{\theta}\|^2$ is minimised when $\boldsymbol{\theta} = \mathbf{a}$ and the theorem is proved.

3.2 Projection matrices

We now show that $\boldsymbol{\theta}_0$ can be obtained by means of a linear transformation $\boldsymbol{\theta}_0 = \mathbf{P}_0\mathbf{y}$ where $\mathbf{P}_0$ is a symmetric idempotent matrix of rank p.

Theorem 3.2.1. If $\boldsymbol{\theta}_0$ is the least squares estimate defined above, then $\boldsymbol{\theta}_0 = \mathbf{P}_0\mathbf{y}$, where $\mathbf{P}_0$ is a symmetric idempotent matrix representing the orthogonal projection of E_n on Ω.

Proof. From Theorem (3.1.1),

$$\begin{aligned} \boldsymbol{\theta}_0 &= \mathbf{a} \\ &= \sum_i c_i \boldsymbol{\alpha}_i \\ &= \sum_i \boldsymbol{\alpha}_i (\mathbf{y}'\boldsymbol{\alpha}_i) \\ &= (\boldsymbol{\alpha}_1, \boldsymbol{\alpha}_2, \ldots, \boldsymbol{\alpha}_p)(\boldsymbol{\alpha}_1, \boldsymbol{\alpha}_2, \ldots, \boldsymbol{\alpha}_p)'\mathbf{y} \\ &= \mathbf{T}\mathbf{T}'\mathbf{y}, \text{ say,} \\ &= \mathbf{P}_0\mathbf{y}. \end{aligned}$$

Now $\mathbf{P}_0' = \mathbf{P}_0$ and $\mathbf{P}_0\mathbf{P}_0 = \mathbf{T}(\mathbf{T}'\mathbf{T})\mathbf{T}' = \mathbf{T}\mathbf{T}' = \mathbf{P}_0$. Hence $\mathbf{P}_0$ is symmetric and idempotent. The converse of this result is also true and we state it as a corollary.

Corollary 3.2.2. If $\mathbf{P}$ is a symmetric $n \times n$ idempotent matrix of rank r, then it represents an orthogonal projection of E_n on some r-dimensional vector space V, say.

Proof. From lemma 1.9.1 we see that $\mathbf{P}$ can be expressed in the form $(\mathbf{s}_1, \ldots, \mathbf{s}_r)(\mathbf{s}_1, \ldots, \mathbf{s}_r)'$ which is the same form as $\mathbf{T}\mathbf{T}'$ above. Hence $\mathbf{P}$ represents an orthogonal projection of E_n on to the vector space spanned by the orthonormal basis $\mathbf{s}_1, \ldots, \mathbf{s}_r$. If this vector space is V, then $\dim[V] = r$ and the proof is complete.

In concluding this section we note that $\boldsymbol{\theta}_0$ is an unbiased estimate of $\boldsymbol{\theta}$ since $E[\boldsymbol{\theta}_0] = \mathbf{P}_0\boldsymbol{\theta} = \boldsymbol{\theta}$; also $D[\boldsymbol{\theta}_0] = \sigma^2\mathbf{P}_0$.

3.3 A useful lemma

In the rest of this book the following simple result will be used often.

Lemma 3.3.1. If V is any vector space contained in E_n and $\mathbf{P}_V$ represents the orthogonal projection of E_n on V, then $R[\mathbf{P}_V] = V$.

Proof. From theorem 3.2.1, $\mathbf{P}_V = \mathbf{T}\mathbf{T}'$ where the columns of $\mathbf{T}$ form an orthonormal basis for V. If $\boldsymbol{\theta} \in V$, $\mathbf{P}_V\boldsymbol{\theta} = \boldsymbol{\theta}$ and $\boldsymbol{\theta} \in R[\mathbf{P}_V]$. Conversely, if $\boldsymbol{\theta} \in R[\mathbf{P}_V]$ then $\boldsymbol{\theta} = \mathbf{T}(\mathbf{T}'\boldsymbol{\alpha})$ for some $\boldsymbol{\alpha}$, and $\boldsymbol{\theta} \in R[\mathbf{T}] = V$. Thus the two vector spaces are equivalent.

3.4 Examples

Example 1. Let $\mathbf{X}$ be an $n \times p$ matrix of rank p such that $\Omega = R[\mathbf{X}] = \{\boldsymbol{\theta} : \boldsymbol{\theta} = \mathbf{X}\boldsymbol{\beta}\}$. Now $\mathbf{P}_0 = \mathbf{T}\mathbf{T}'$ where the columns of $\mathbf{T}$ form an orthonormal basis of Ω. Since the columns of $\mathbf{X}$ also form a basis of Ω, $\mathbf{X} = \mathbf{T}\mathbf{C}$, where $\mathbf{C}$ is a non-singular matrix. Hence $\mathbf{P}_0 = \mathbf{X}(\mathbf{C}'\mathbf{C})^{-1}\mathbf{X}' = \mathbf{X}(\mathbf{X}'\mathbf{X})^{-1}\mathbf{X}'$. If $\boldsymbol{\beta}_0$ is defined by $\boldsymbol{\theta}_0 = \mathbf{X}\boldsymbol{\beta}_0$, then

$$\boldsymbol{\beta}_0 = (\mathbf{X}'\mathbf{X})^{-1}\mathbf{X}'\boldsymbol{\theta}_0 = (\mathbf{X}'\mathbf{X})^{-1}\mathbf{X}'\mathbf{y}$$

and

$$E[\boldsymbol{\beta}_0] = (\mathbf{X}'\mathbf{X})^{-1}\mathbf{X}'\boldsymbol{\theta} = \boldsymbol{\beta}$$

$$D[\boldsymbol{\beta}_0] = \sigma^2(\mathbf{X}'\mathbf{X})^{-1}.$$

These results can also be derived by the more familiar method of minimising the sum of squares (s.s.), $\|\mathbf{y} - \boldsymbol{\theta}\|^2$ for $\boldsymbol{\theta} \in \Omega$; thus we wish to minimise s.s. $= (\mathbf{y} - \mathbf{X}\boldsymbol{\beta})'(\mathbf{y} - \mathbf{X}\boldsymbol{\beta})$ for $\boldsymbol{\beta}$. If $d/d\boldsymbol{\beta}$ denotes the column vector with ith element $d/d\beta_i$, then

$$\frac{d(\boldsymbol{\beta}'\mathbf{X}'\mathbf{y})}{d\boldsymbol{\beta}} = \mathbf{X}'\mathbf{y} \quad \text{and} \quad \frac{d(\boldsymbol{\beta}'\mathbf{X}'\mathbf{X}\boldsymbol{\beta})}{d\boldsymbol{\beta}} = 2\mathbf{X}'\mathbf{X}\boldsymbol{\beta}$$

giving

$$\frac{d(\text{s.s.})}{d\boldsymbol{\beta}} = 2\mathbf{X}'\mathbf{X}\boldsymbol{\beta} - 2\mathbf{X}'\mathbf{y} = 0. \tag{3.4.1}$$

These equations are known as the *least squares* or *normal* equations and have the solution $\boldsymbol{\beta}_0 = (\mathbf{X}'\mathbf{X})^{-1}\mathbf{X}'\mathbf{y}$ as before.

Example 2. Suppose that $\Omega = R[\mathbf{X}]$ but now $\mathbf{X}$ is $n \times r$ and of rank p $(p < r)$. This means that although $\boldsymbol{\theta}$ is uniquely defined in $\boldsymbol{\theta} = \mathbf{X}\boldsymbol{\beta}$, $\boldsymbol{\beta}$ is not, as the columns of $\mathbf{X}$ are linearly dependent. In this situation we say that $\boldsymbol{\beta}$ is *non-identifiable* and the least squares equations (3.4.1) do not have a unique solution for $\boldsymbol{\beta}$ as $\mathbf{X}'\mathbf{X}$ is singular. To overcome this we introduce a set of t constraints $\mathbf{H}\boldsymbol{\beta} = \mathbf{0}$ on $\boldsymbol{\beta}$ satisfying two necessary and sufficient conditions for identifiability; namely (i) for every $\boldsymbol{\theta} \in \Omega$ there exists a $\boldsymbol{\beta}$ such that $\boldsymbol{\theta} = \mathbf{X}\boldsymbol{\beta}$ and $\mathbf{H}\boldsymbol{\beta} = \mathbf{0}$, and (ii) this value of $\boldsymbol{\beta}$ is unique. The first condition is equivalent to $R[\mathbf{X}'] \cap R[\mathbf{H}'] = \mathbf{0}$, that is, no vector which is a linear combination of the rows of $\mathbf{X}$ is also a linear combination of the rows of $\mathbf{H}$ except $\mathbf{0}$ (for proof see Appendix I, lemma 3). The second condition is satisfied if the rank of the augmented matrix $\mathbf{G}' = (\mathbf{X}', \mathbf{H}')$ is r, for then the $r \times r$ matrix $\mathbf{G}'\mathbf{G} = \mathbf{X}'\mathbf{X} + \mathbf{H}'\mathbf{H}$ is non-singular and the unique value of $\boldsymbol{\beta}$ is given by $\boldsymbol{\beta} = (\mathbf{G}'\mathbf{G})^{-1}\mathbf{X}'\boldsymbol{\theta}$. Thus, combining these two results, the conditions $\mathbf{H}\boldsymbol{\beta} = \mathbf{0}$ are suitable for identifiability if and only if rank$[\mathbf{G}] = r$ and rank$[\mathbf{H}] = r - p$. In general we can assume that there are no redundant identifiability constraints, i.e. $t = r - p$ and the rows of $\mathbf{H}$ are linearly independent.

From §1.6 and equation (3.4.1), the least squares equations are given by

$$\begin{aligned} 2\mathbf{X}'\mathbf{X}\boldsymbol{\beta}_0 - 2\mathbf{X}'\mathbf{y} + \mathbf{H}'\boldsymbol{\mu} &= \mathbf{0} \\ \mathbf{H}\boldsymbol{\beta}_0 &= \mathbf{0}, \end{aligned} \tag{3.4.2}$$

where $\boldsymbol{\mu}$ is the Lagrange multiplier. This leads to

Theorem 3.4.1. If the constraints $\mathbf{H}\boldsymbol{\beta} = \mathbf{0}$ are suitable for identifiability and $t = r - p$, then (i) $\mathbf{P}_0 = \mathbf{X}(\mathbf{X}'\mathbf{X} + \mathbf{H}'\mathbf{H})^{-1}\mathbf{X}'$, (ii) $\boldsymbol{\mu} = \mathbf{0}$, and (iii) $\boldsymbol{\beta}_0 = (\mathbf{X}'\mathbf{X} + \mathbf{H}'\mathbf{H})^{-1}\mathbf{X}'\mathbf{y}$.

Proof. Since the constraints are suitable for identifiability, it follows that for every $\boldsymbol{\theta} \in R[\mathbf{X}]$, $(\boldsymbol{\theta}', \mathbf{0}')' = \mathbf{G}\boldsymbol{\beta}$ for some unique $\boldsymbol{\beta}$. This implies that $(\boldsymbol{\theta}', \mathbf{0}')' \in R[\mathbf{G}]$ for every $\boldsymbol{\theta} \in R[\mathbf{X}]$, and from Example 1 above,

$$\mathbf{G}(\mathbf{G}'\mathbf{G})^{-1}\mathbf{G}'\begin{bmatrix}\boldsymbol{\theta} \\ \mathbf{0}\end{bmatrix} = \begin{bmatrix}\boldsymbol{\theta} \\ \mathbf{0}\end{bmatrix}$$

since $\mathbf{G}(\mathbf{G}'\mathbf{G})^{-1}\mathbf{G}'$ represents the projection of E_{n+t} onto $R[\mathbf{G}]$. Hence

$$\begin{aligned} \mathbf{X}(\mathbf{G}'\mathbf{G})^{-1}\mathbf{X}'\boldsymbol{\theta} &= \boldsymbol{\theta} \\ \text{and} \qquad \mathbf{H}(\mathbf{G}'\mathbf{G})^{-1}\mathbf{X}'\boldsymbol{\theta} &= \mathbf{0} \end{aligned} \tag{3.4.3}$$

for every $\boldsymbol{\theta} \in R[\mathbf{X}]$. Therefore

$$R[\mathbf{X}(\mathbf{G}'\mathbf{G})^{-1}\mathbf{H}'] \perp R[\mathbf{X}],$$

and as the left-hand side is contained in the right-hand side,

$$\mathbf{H}(\mathbf{G}'\mathbf{G})^{-1}\mathbf{X}' = \mathbf{0}. \tag{3.4.4}$$

Also, using this equation we find that $\mathbf{X}(\mathbf{G}'\mathbf{G})^{-1}\mathbf{X}'$ is symmetric and idempotent and therefore represents the projection of E_n onto some vector space V, say. From equation (3.4.3) $V \supset R[\mathbf{X}]$, but from lemma 3.3.1

$$V = R[\mathbf{X}(\mathbf{G}'\mathbf{G})^{-1}\mathbf{X}'] \subset R[\mathbf{X}].$$

Hence $\quad V = R[\mathbf{X}] = \Omega \quad$ and $\quad \mathbf{P}_0 = \mathbf{X}(\mathbf{G}'\mathbf{G})^{-1}\mathbf{X}'$.

Solving the least squares equations for $\boldsymbol{\beta}_0$, setting $\mathbf{H}\boldsymbol{\beta}_0 = \mathbf{0}$ and using equation (3.4.4) gives $\mathbf{H}(\mathbf{G}'\mathbf{G})^{-1}\mathbf{H}'\boldsymbol{\mu} = \mathbf{0}$. As $\mathbf{H}$ has full rank and $\mathbf{G}'\mathbf{G}$ is positive definite, $\mathbf{H}(\mathbf{G}'\mathbf{G})^{-1}\mathbf{H}'$ is non-singular (Appendix I, lemma 2), thus $\boldsymbol{\mu} = \mathbf{0}$. It then follows that $\boldsymbol{\beta}_0 = (\mathbf{G}'\mathbf{G})^{-1}\mathbf{X}'\mathbf{y}$ and this completes the proof of the theorem.

EXERCISE 6. Prove that $E[\boldsymbol{\beta}_0] = \boldsymbol{\beta}$.

Obviously the matrix $\mathbf{H}$ is not unique, and we now turn our attention to the practical problem of finding a suitable $\mathbf{H}$ when $\mathbf{X}$ is given. The method we give is due to Plackett (1950) and uses the following lemmas.

Lemma 3.4.2. If $\mathbf{X}$ is an $n \times r$ matrix of rank $p\,(r - p = t > 0)$, then there exists an $r \times t$ matrix $\mathbf{D}$ of rank t such that $\mathbf{X}\mathbf{D} = \mathbf{0}$.

Proof. Since $\mathbf{X}$ has rank p, we can partition it in the form

$$\mathbf{X} = \begin{bmatrix} \mathbf{X}_{p,p} \,, & \mathbf{X}_{p,t} \\ \mathbf{X}_{n-p,p} \,, & \mathbf{X}_{n-p,t} \end{bmatrix},$$

the suffices of the matrix elements indicating the numbers of rows and columns. We can assume, without loss of generality, that $\mathbf{X}_{p,p}$ is non-singular and therefore the rows of $\mathbf{X}$ are linearly dependent on the first p rows, that is

$$(\mathbf{X}_{n-p,p}\,,\ \mathbf{X}_{n-p,t}) = \mathbf{C}(\mathbf{X}_{p,p}\,,\ \mathbf{X}_{p,t})$$

for some matrix $\mathbf{C}$. Define the $r \times t$ matrix

$$\mathbf{D} = \begin{bmatrix} \mathbf{X}_{p,p}^{-1}\mathbf{X}_{p,t} \\ -\mathbf{I}_t \end{bmatrix}$$

which obviously has rank t. Then $\mathbf{X}\mathbf{D} = \mathbf{0}$ and the lemma is proved. We note that if $\mathbf{U} = (\mathbf{u}_1, \mathbf{u}_2, \ldots, \mathbf{u}_t)$ is a $t \times t$ non-singular matrix then $\mathbf{X}\mathbf{D}\mathbf{U} = \mathbf{0}$ and therefore $\mathbf{D}$ is not unique.

Lemma 3.4.3. If $\mathbf{H}$ is a $t \times r$ matrix of rank t such that $\mathbf{H}\mathbf{D}$ is non-singular then $(\mathbf{X}'\mathbf{X} + \mathbf{H}'\mathbf{H})$ is also non-singular.

Proof. Consider
$$\begin{aligned} Q &= \boldsymbol{\beta}'(\mathbf{X}'\mathbf{X} + \mathbf{H}'\mathbf{H})\boldsymbol{\beta} \\ &= (\mathbf{X}\boldsymbol{\beta})'(\mathbf{X}\boldsymbol{\beta}) + (\mathbf{H}\boldsymbol{\beta})'(\mathbf{H}\boldsymbol{\beta}). \end{aligned}$$

Putting $\mathbf{x} = \mathbf{G}\boldsymbol{\beta}$, where $\mathbf{G}$ is defined as above, gives $Q = \mathbf{x}'\mathbf{x} \geqslant 0$. The only *non-zero* vectors $\boldsymbol{\beta}$ making $\mathbf{X}\boldsymbol{\beta} = \mathbf{0}$ are columns or linear combinations of columns of $\mathbf{D}\mathbf{U}$, since $\mathbf{X}\mathbf{D}\mathbf{U} = \mathbf{0}$. But then $\mathbf{H}\mathbf{D}\mathbf{u}_i$ and therefore $\mathbf{H}\boldsymbol{\beta}$ is non-zero since $\mathbf{H}\mathbf{D}$ is non-singular. Therefore $Q \neq 0$ when $\boldsymbol{\beta} \neq \mathbf{0}$ and Q is positive definite. This implies that $(\mathbf{X}'\mathbf{X} + \mathbf{H}'\mathbf{H})$ is non-singular and the proof is complete.

We note that the matrix $\mathbf{H}$ so chosen satisfies the identifiability conditions, namely $\text{rank}[\mathbf{H}] = t = r-p$ and $\text{rank}[\mathbf{G}] = r$. Thus the method is to find $\mathbf{D}$ such that $\mathbf{XD} = \mathbf{0}$ and then $\mathbf{H}$ such that $\mathbf{HD}$ is non-singular. Also, using this approach, the dispersion matrix for the least squares estimate $\boldsymbol{\beta}_0$ can now be given in a simpler form. Since

$$(\mathbf{X}'\mathbf{X} + \mathbf{H}'\mathbf{H})\mathbf{D} = \mathbf{H}'\mathbf{H}\mathbf{D},$$

then

$$\mathbf{D}(\mathbf{HD})^{-1} = (\mathbf{X}'\mathbf{X} + \mathbf{H}'\mathbf{H})^{-1}\mathbf{H}'.$$

Hence

$$\mathbf{I}_r - \mathbf{D}(\mathbf{HD})^{-1}\mathbf{H} = (\mathbf{G}'\mathbf{G})^{-1}\mathbf{X}'\mathbf{X}$$

and

$$\begin{aligned} D[\boldsymbol{\beta}_0] &= \sigma^2(\mathbf{G}'\mathbf{G})^{-1}\mathbf{X}'\mathbf{X}(\mathbf{G}'\mathbf{G})^{-1} \\ &= \sigma^2(\mathbf{I}_r - \mathbf{D}(\mathbf{HD})^{-1}\mathbf{H})(\mathbf{G}'\mathbf{G})^{-1}. \end{aligned}$$

For examples of this method, cf. Plackett (1960a, p. 44), Kendall and Stuart (1961, exercise 19.9) and Freeman and Jeffers (1962).

Instead of introducing identifiability constraints, another approach to this problem of identifiability of $\boldsymbol{\beta}$ is to find out what functions of $\boldsymbol{\beta}$ are estimable. A linear function $\mathbf{c}'\boldsymbol{\beta}$ is said to be *estimable* if it has a linear unbiased estimate $\mathbf{a}'\mathbf{y}$. Thus

$$\mathbf{a}'\mathbf{X}\boldsymbol{\beta} = E[\mathbf{a}'\mathbf{y}] = \mathbf{c}'\boldsymbol{\beta}$$

is an identity in $\boldsymbol{\beta}$, and $\mathbf{c}' = \mathbf{a}'\mathbf{X}$. Hence $\mathbf{c}'\boldsymbol{\beta}$ is an estimable function of $\boldsymbol{\beta}$ if and only if $\mathbf{c}$ is a linear combination of the rows of $\mathbf{X}$. Since $\mathbf{c}'\boldsymbol{\beta} = \mathbf{a}'\boldsymbol{\theta}$, the class of estimable functions is simply the class of all linear functions $\mathbf{a}'\boldsymbol{\theta}$ of the mean vector.

This approach using estimable functions is described in Scheffé (1959), Graybill (1961) and in particular, Chakrabarti (1962). However, in practice one usually has to introduce some constraints on $\boldsymbol{\beta}$ in order to obtain a solution of the least squares equations.

Another approach is to use the generalised inverse (cf. §3.8).

Example 3. Let $\Omega = N[\mathbf{A}]$, where the rows of $\mathbf{A}$ are linearly independent. Then $\mathbf{I}_n - \mathbf{P}_0$ represents the projection of E_n on $\Omega^\perp$ since $\mathbf{y} = \mathbf{P}_0\mathbf{y} + (\mathbf{I} - \mathbf{P}_0)\mathbf{y}$. As $\Omega^\perp = R[\mathbf{A}']$ (lemma 1.2.1), it follows from example 1 that

$$\mathbf{P}_0 = \mathbf{I}_n - \mathbf{A}'(\mathbf{AA}')^{-1}\mathbf{A}.$$

Example 4. Suppose that $y_1, y_2, \ldots, y_n$ are independent observations from $\mathcal{N}[\mu, \sigma^2]$. Thus $\mathbf{y} = \boldsymbol{\theta} + \mathbf{e}$ where $\mathbf{e}$ is $\mathcal{N}[\mathbf{0}, \sigma^2\mathbf{I}_n]$ and $\boldsymbol{\theta} = \mathbf{1}_n\mu$. As $\Omega = R[\mathbf{1}_n]$, $\mathbf{P}_0 = \mathbf{1}_n(\mathbf{1}_n'\mathbf{1}_n)^{-1}\mathbf{1}_n' = n^{-1}\mathbf{1}_n\mathbf{1}_n'$. Therefore

$$\boldsymbol{\theta}_0 = \mathbf{P}_0\mathbf{y} = \mathbf{1}_n\bar{y}.$$

and

$$\mu_0 = (\mathbf{1}_n'\mathbf{1}_n)^{-1}\mathbf{1}_n'\mathbf{1}_n\bar{y}. = \bar{y}..$$

Example 5. Suppose that $\mathbf{y} = \mathbf{X}\boldsymbol{\beta} + \boldsymbol{\delta}$ and $D[\boldsymbol{\delta}] = \sigma^2 \mathbf{B}$, where $\mathbf{X}$ has full rank and $\mathbf{B}$ is a known positive definite matrix. To find the least squares estimate $\boldsymbol{\beta}_0$ we can transform the model to the standard form

$$\mathbf{z} = \boldsymbol{\phi} + \mathbf{e}, \quad D[\mathbf{e}] = \sigma^2 \mathbf{I}_n$$

using the transformation $\mathbf{z} = \mathbf{V}^{-1}\mathbf{y}$, $\boldsymbol{\phi} = \mathbf{V}^{-1}\mathbf{X}\boldsymbol{\beta}$, where $\mathbf{V}$ is given by $\mathbf{B} = \mathbf{V}\mathbf{V}'$ (§2.3). We now minimise $(\mathbf{z} - \mathbf{V}^{-1}\mathbf{X}\boldsymbol{\beta})'(\mathbf{z} - \mathbf{V}^{-1}\mathbf{X}\boldsymbol{\beta})$ or $(\mathbf{y} - \mathbf{X}\boldsymbol{\beta})'\mathbf{B}^{-1}(\mathbf{y} - \mathbf{X}\boldsymbol{\beta})$ with respect to $\boldsymbol{\beta}$. In practice it is usually simpler to work with the original observations $\mathbf{y}$ and minimise the above weighted s.s. rather than calculate the transformed observations $\mathbf{z}$. In many applications $\mathbf{B} = \text{diag}(w_1, w_2, \ldots, w_n)$ and our s.s. to be minimised takes the form $\sum_{i=1}^{n} w_i^{-1}(y_i - \theta_i)^2$, where the w_i are suitably chosen weights. For examples of the use of weighted least squares cf. Scheffé (1959) (§3.8) and Quenouille (1952) (§7.7). Another application of this theory is in the ordered least squares estimation of location and scale parameters (Kendall and Stuart, 1961, §19.18).

3.5 Gauss–Markov theorem

Having given one method of estimating $\boldsymbol{\theta}$, namely by a least squares procedure, we might now ask if there are better ways of estimating this quantity. Our question is partly answered by the following theorem (due to Gauss) which proves that the least squares estimate is best in a certain sense. The proof of the theorem is based on Scheffé (1959, p. 13) and is essentially a generalisation of an approach given by Durbin and Kendall (1951).

Theorem 3.5.1. If $\boldsymbol{\theta} \in \Omega$ and $c = \mathbf{a}'\boldsymbol{\theta}$, then among the class of linear unbiased estimates of c there exists a unique estimate $c_0 = \mathbf{a}'\mathbf{P}_0\mathbf{y}$ which has minimum variance. Thus if $\mathbf{b}'\mathbf{y}$ is any other linear unbiased estimate of c then $E[\mathbf{b}'\mathbf{y}] = c$ and $\text{Var}[\mathbf{b}'\mathbf{y}] > \text{Var}[c_0]$.

Proof. Since $\mathbf{P}_0\boldsymbol{\theta} = \boldsymbol{\theta}$ and $\mathbf{a} = \mathbf{P}_0\mathbf{a} + (\mathbf{I}_n - \mathbf{P}_0)\mathbf{a}$,

$$\begin{aligned} c &= E[\mathbf{a}'\mathbf{y}] \\ &= E[(\mathbf{P}_0\mathbf{a})'\mathbf{y}] + \mathbf{a}'(\mathbf{I}_n - \mathbf{P}_0)\boldsymbol{\theta} \\ &= E[c_0]. \end{aligned}$$

Thus c_0 is a linear unbiased estimate of c.

Let $\mathbf{b}'\mathbf{y}$ be any other unbiased estimate of c; then by a similar argument $(\mathbf{P}_0\mathbf{b})'\mathbf{y}$ is also an unbiased estimate. Now

$$\begin{aligned} 0 &= E[(\mathbf{P}_0\mathbf{a} - \mathbf{P}_0\mathbf{b})'\mathbf{y}] \\ &= (\mathbf{P}_0\mathbf{a} - \mathbf{P}_0\mathbf{b})'\boldsymbol{\theta} \end{aligned}$$

for every $\boldsymbol{\theta} \in \Omega$, and hence $(\mathbf{P}_0\mathbf{a} - \mathbf{P}_0\mathbf{b}) \in \Omega^{\perp}$.

But this vector belongs to Ω, and hence $\mathbf{P}_0\mathbf{a} = \mathbf{P}_0\mathbf{b}$ for every $\mathbf{b}$; we have thus shown that c_0 is unique. Also

$$\begin{aligned} \text{Var}[\mathbf{b}'\mathbf{y}] &= \sigma^2 \|\mathbf{b}\|^2 \\ &= \sigma^2(\|\mathbf{P}_0\mathbf{b}\|^2 + \|(\mathbf{I}_n - \mathbf{P}_0)\mathbf{b}\|^2) \\ &\geqslant \sigma^2\|\mathbf{P}_0\mathbf{b}\|^2 \\ &= \text{Var}[c_0]. \end{aligned}$$

Thus c_0 is unique and has minimum variance for the class of unbiased estimates.

Corollary. Let θ_i be the ith element of $\boldsymbol{\theta}$ and let $\mathbf{a}$ be the unit vector with the ith element unity and the other elements zero. Then the linear unbiased estimate of $\theta_i = \mathbf{a}'\boldsymbol{\theta}$ with minimum variance is $\theta_{i0} = \mathbf{a}'\mathbf{P}_0\mathbf{y} = \mathbf{a}'\boldsymbol{\theta}_0$, i.e. the least squares estimate of θ_i.

3.6 The logic of least squares

In the Gauss–Markov theorem we restricted ourselves to the class of linear unbiased estimates of $\mathbf{a}'\boldsymbol{\theta}$ and showed that $\mathbf{a}'\boldsymbol{\theta}_0$ is the unique member of this class having minimum variance. Barnard (1963) has pointed out that in some situations the condition of unbiasedness may not be a reasonable requirement to impose. A simple example which illustrates this is given by the geometric distribution

$$Pr\{x = r\} = (1-\phi)^{r-1}\phi, \quad r = 1, 2, \ldots$$

with $0 < \phi < 1$. The *unique* unbiased estimate of ϕ, namely

$$f(x) = \begin{cases} 1, & x = 1 \\ 0, & x > 1 \end{cases}$$

is an absurd estimate as it lies outside the range of possible values of ϕ. Barnard suggests replacing the unbiasedness assumption by the more reasonable assumption that the range of $\mathbf{a}'\boldsymbol{\theta}$ is unbounded. A slight generalisation of his argument is as follows.

The mean square error of any linear estimate $\mathbf{d}'\mathbf{y}$ of $\mathbf{a}'\boldsymbol{\theta}$ is given by

$$\begin{aligned} E[(\mathbf{d}'\mathbf{y} - \mathbf{a}'\boldsymbol{\theta})^2] &= E[(\mathbf{d}'\mathbf{y} - \mathbf{d}'\boldsymbol{\theta} + \mathbf{d}'\boldsymbol{\theta} - \mathbf{a}'\boldsymbol{\theta})^2], \\ &= \mathbf{d}'\mathbf{d}\sigma^2 + (\mathbf{d}'\boldsymbol{\theta} - \mathbf{a}'\boldsymbol{\theta})^2. \end{aligned}$$

Now if the range of $\mathbf{a}'\boldsymbol{\theta}$ is unbounded then the second term in this expression is unbounded unless $\mathbf{d}'\boldsymbol{\theta} - \mathbf{a}'\boldsymbol{\theta} = 0$ for every $\boldsymbol{\theta} \in \Omega$, that is unless $(\mathbf{d}' - \mathbf{a}')\mathbf{P}_0 = \mathbf{0}'$ (lemma 3.3.1). This implies that

$$\begin{aligned} \mathbf{d}'\mathbf{d} &= \|\mathbf{P}_0\mathbf{d}\|^2 + \|(\mathbf{I} - \mathbf{P}_0)\mathbf{d}\|^2 \\ &= \|\mathbf{P}_0\mathbf{a}\|^2 + \|(\mathbf{I} - \mathbf{P}_0)\mathbf{d}\|^2 \end{aligned}$$

and has a minimum value of $\|\mathbf{P}_0\mathbf{a}\|^2$ when $\mathbf{d} = \mathbf{P}_0\mathbf{d} = \mathbf{P}_0\mathbf{a}$. Thus if the range of $\mathbf{a}'\boldsymbol{\theta}$ is unbounded, then among all linear estimates of $\mathbf{a}'\boldsymbol{\theta}$ having bounded mean square error, the least squares estimate $\mathbf{a}'\mathbf{P}_0\mathbf{y}$ has minimum mean square error.

The condition of unboundedness is a very reasonable restriction as it is usually assumed in practical applications of the Gauss–Markov theorem. The reason for this is that if the range of $\mathbf{a}'\boldsymbol{\theta}$ is bounded it is perfectly possible for the least squares estimate to lie outside the bounds.

3.7 Estimation of σ^2

Having replaced $\boldsymbol{\theta}$ by its best linear unbiased estimate $\boldsymbol{\theta}_0$ we would expect the residual s.s., $(\mathbf{y}-\boldsymbol{\theta}_0)'(\mathbf{y}-\boldsymbol{\theta}_0)$, to provide some estimate of σ^2. Now

$$\begin{aligned}(\mathbf{y}-\boldsymbol{\theta}_0)'(\mathbf{y}-\boldsymbol{\theta}_0) &= \mathbf{y}'(\mathbf{I}-\mathbf{P}_0)^2\mathbf{y}, \\ &= \mathbf{y}'(\mathbf{I}-\mathbf{P}_0)\mathbf{y}.\end{aligned}$$

For any symmetric matrix $\mathbf{A}$,

$$\begin{aligned}E[(\mathbf{y}-\boldsymbol{\theta})'\mathbf{A}(\mathbf{y}-\boldsymbol{\theta})] &= E[\sum_i\sum_j(y_i-\theta_i)(y_j-\theta_j)a_{ij}] \\ &= \sigma^2\sum_i a_{ii} \\ &= \sigma^2\,\mathrm{tr}[\mathbf{A}].\end{aligned}$$

Since

$$\mathbf{y}'\mathbf{A}\mathbf{y} = (\mathbf{y}-\boldsymbol{\theta})'\mathbf{A}(\mathbf{y}-\boldsymbol{\theta}) + 2\boldsymbol{\theta}'\mathbf{A}\mathbf{y} - \boldsymbol{\theta}'\mathbf{A}\boldsymbol{\theta}$$

then

$$E[\mathbf{y}'\mathbf{A}\mathbf{y}] = \sigma^2\,\mathrm{tr}[\mathbf{A}] + \boldsymbol{\theta}'\mathbf{A}\boldsymbol{\theta}. \qquad (3.7.1)$$

As $\mathbf{A}$ is symmetric, there exists an orthogonal matrix $\mathbf{T}$ such that $\mathbf{T}'\mathbf{A}\mathbf{T} = \mathrm{diag}(\lambda_1, \lambda_2, \ldots, \lambda_n)$ where $\lambda_1, \lambda_2, \ldots, \lambda_n$ are the eigen values of $\mathbf{A}$. Hence

$$\begin{aligned}\sum_i \lambda_i &= \mathrm{tr}[\mathbf{T}'(\mathbf{A}\mathbf{T})] \\ &= \mathrm{tr}[(\mathbf{A}\mathbf{T})\mathbf{T}'] \\ &= \mathrm{tr}[\mathbf{A}].\end{aligned}$$

Applying these results to the residual s.s. gives, from equation (3.7.1),

$$E[\mathbf{y}'(\mathbf{I}-\mathbf{P}_0)\mathbf{y}] = \sigma^2(n-p)$$

since $(\mathbf{I}-\mathbf{P}_0)$ represents the projection of E_n on $\Omega^\perp$ and is therefore of rank $n-p$ (lemmas 1.5.1 and 3.3.1). Thus $s^2 = \mathbf{y}'(\mathbf{I}-\mathbf{P}_0)\mathbf{y}/(n-p)$ is an unbiased quadratic estimate of σ^2.

It is natural to ask whether s^2 has any optimal properties similar to those of $\boldsymbol{\theta}_0$, namely, among all unbiased quadratic estimates of σ^2 does s^2 have the minimum variance? This question is discussed fully in Plackett (1960a) and Atiqullah (1962) and the following conclusions are reached.

Let $\mathbf{y}'\mathbf{A}\mathbf{y}$ be an unbiased estimate of $(n-p)\sigma^2$ and let p_{ij} be the i,jth element of $\mathbf{P}_0$. We assume that each error e_i has the same distribution and therefore the same kurtosis γ_2, where $\gamma_2 = E[e_i^4]/\sigma^4 - 3$. Then s^2 is the best quadratic unbiased estimate of σ^2

(i) for any $\mathbf{A}$, if and only if $\gamma_2 = 0$;

(ii) for any γ_2 if and only if

$$(n-p)\sum_{r=1}^{n} p_{rr}p_{rs}^2 = p_{ss}\sum_{r=1}^{n} p_{rr}^2 \quad \text{for } s = 1, 2, \ldots, n;$$

(iii) for any positive semi-definite $\mathbf{A}$ if the diagonal elements p_{rr} are all equal. If $\mathbf{e}$ is $\mathcal{N}[\mathbf{0}, \sigma^2\mathbf{I}_n]$ then $\gamma_2 = 0$ and s^2 is the best estimate for any $\mathbf{A}$. The restriction, first introduced by Rao (1952), that $\mathbf{A}$ should be positive semidefinite is a very reasonable one since $\sigma^2 \geqslant 0$.

3.8 Related topics

From theorem 3.4.1 we have

$$\boldsymbol{\beta}_0 = (\mathbf{X}'\mathbf{X} + \mathbf{H}'\mathbf{H})^{-1}\mathbf{X}'\mathbf{y},$$

where $(\mathbf{X}'\mathbf{X} + \mathbf{H}'\mathbf{H})^{-1}$ is called a pseudo-inverse or generalised inverse (g-inverse) of $\mathbf{X}'\mathbf{X}$. This g-inverse is not unique, and another possibility is $\boldsymbol{\beta}_0 = \mathbf{B}_{11}\mathbf{X}'\mathbf{y}$ where

$$\begin{bmatrix} \mathbf{X}'\mathbf{X}, & \mathbf{H}' \\ \mathbf{H}\ , & \mathbf{0} \end{bmatrix}^{-1} = \begin{bmatrix} \mathbf{B}_{11}, & \mathbf{B}_{12} \\ \mathbf{B}_{21}, & \mathbf{B}_{22} \end{bmatrix}.$$

For further discussion on this question cf. Rao (1962), John (1964) and Chipman (1964).

A quick estimate of the variance σ^2 can be obtained from the range of the sample, and the reader is referred to Pearson and Hartley (1956) and Harter (1959) for details. A particular application is in the use of control charts for stabilising the mean and variance of a process (Davies, 1961).

CHAPTER 4

HYPOTHESIS TESTING

4.1 Maximum likelihood estimation

Given the model $\mathbf{y} = \boldsymbol{\theta} + \mathbf{e}$, where $\boldsymbol{\theta} \in \Omega$, a p-dimensional subspace of E_n, we now consider the problem of testing the hypothesis H that $\boldsymbol{\theta} \in \omega$, a $p-q$-dimensional subspace of Ω. In order to construct a test statistic for H, we assume that $\mathbf{y}$ is $\mathscr{N}[\boldsymbol{\theta}, \sigma^2 \mathbf{I}_n]$ and the likelihood takes the form

$$L_y[\boldsymbol{\theta}, \sigma^2] = (2\pi\sigma^2)^{-n/2} \exp\{-(\mathbf{y}-\boldsymbol{\theta})'(\mathbf{y}-\boldsymbol{\theta})/2\sigma^2\}.$$

Let $\sup(\boldsymbol{\theta} \in \Omega)\, L_y[\boldsymbol{\theta}, \sigma^2]$ represent the maximum value of the likelihood function with respect to σ^2 and $\boldsymbol{\theta}$, where $\boldsymbol{\theta} \in \Omega$ or equivalently $\mathbf{P}_0\boldsymbol{\theta} = \boldsymbol{\theta}$. The values of σ^2 and $\boldsymbol{\theta}$ which maximise the likelihood function are called the maximum likelihood estimates and can be found most easily by maximising $\log L_y[\boldsymbol{\theta}, \sigma^2]$. Differentiating this with respect to σ^2 and $\boldsymbol{\theta}$ and introducing a Lagrange multiplier $\boldsymbol{\mu}$ for the constraints $(\mathbf{I} - \mathbf{P}_0)\boldsymbol{\theta} = \mathbf{0}$, gives (cf. equation 3.4.2)

$$-n/2\sigma^2 + (\mathbf{y}-\boldsymbol{\theta})'(\mathbf{y}-\boldsymbol{\theta})/2\sigma^4 = 0$$

$$-\mathbf{y} + \boldsymbol{\theta} + (\mathbf{I}-\mathbf{P}_0)\boldsymbol{\mu}\sigma^2 = \mathbf{0} \qquad (4.1.1)$$

and

$$(\mathbf{I} - \mathbf{P})\boldsymbol{\theta} = \mathbf{0}.$$

Premultiplying equation (4.1.1) by $\mathbf{P}_0$ leads to the maximum likelihood estimates $\boldsymbol{\theta}_0 = \mathbf{P}_0\mathbf{y}$ and

$$\sigma_0^2 = (\mathbf{y}-\boldsymbol{\theta}_0)'(\mathbf{y}-\boldsymbol{\theta}_0)/n = \mathbf{y}'(\mathbf{I}-\mathbf{P}_0)\mathbf{y}/n.$$

We note that the maximum likelihood estimate of $\boldsymbol{\theta}$ is just the usual least squares estimate $\boldsymbol{\theta}_0$ while σ_0^2 is a biased estimate of σ^2. However, as $\sigma_0^2 = s^2(n-p)/n$, where s^2 is the unbiased least squares estimate of σ^2, $\sigma_0^2 \to s^2$ as $n \to \infty$ and therefore σ_0^2 is a consistent estimate of σ^2, since it can be shown that $\operatorname{var}[\sigma_0^2] \to 0$.

4.2 The *F* test

The usual test statistic for H is based on the likelihood ratio $L[H \mid G]$ where

$$L[H \mid G] = \frac{\sup(\boldsymbol{\theta} \in \omega)\, L_y[\boldsymbol{\theta}, \sigma^2]}{\sup(\boldsymbol{\theta} \in \Omega)\, L_y[\boldsymbol{\theta}, \sigma^2]}$$

and we accept H if $L[H \mid G]$ is "near" enough to unity. Any monotonic function of $L[H|G]$ would also be suitable as a test statistic, and for reasons which we shall see later we choose

$$F = (\{L[H|G]\}^{-2/n} - 1)(n-p)/q.$$

We would now accept H if F is "small" enough.

Let σ_1^2, $\boldsymbol{\theta}_1$ be the maximum likelihood estimates for $\boldsymbol{\theta} \in \omega$; then $\boldsymbol{\theta}_1 = \mathbf{P}_1\mathbf{y}$ and $\sigma_1^2 = \|\mathbf{y}-\boldsymbol{\theta}_1\|^2/n$, where $\mathbf{P}_1$ represents the projection of E_n on ω. Thus

$$L[H|G] = (\sigma_0^2/\sigma_1^2)^{n/2}$$

and

$$\begin{aligned} F &= \frac{(n-p)}{q}\frac{(\sigma_1^2-\sigma_0^2)}{\sigma_0^2} \\ &= \frac{(n-p)}{q}\frac{\mathbf{y}'(\mathbf{P}_0-\mathbf{P}_1)\mathbf{y}}{\mathbf{y}'(\mathbf{I}-\mathbf{P}_0)\mathbf{y}} \\ &= \frac{(n-p)}{q}\frac{(Q_1-Q_0)}{Q_0}, \text{ say,} \end{aligned}$$

where $Q_i = \mathbf{y}'(\mathbf{I}-\mathbf{P}_i)\mathbf{y}$ $(i = 0, 1)$. To find the distribution of F we shall require the following lemma.

Lemma 4.2.1. Suppose $\mathbf{A}_1, \mathbf{A}_2, \ldots, \mathbf{A}_m$ is a sequence of symmetric $n \times n$ matrices such that $\sum_i \mathbf{A}_i = \mathbf{I}_n$, then the following conditions are equivalent:

(i) $\sum_i \text{rank}[\mathbf{A}_i] = n$,

(ii) $\mathbf{A}_i\mathbf{A}_j = \mathbf{0}$ for $i \neq j$,

(iii) $\mathbf{A}_i^2 = \mathbf{A}_i$ for $i = 1, 2, \ldots, m$.

A proof of this lemma is given in Appendix I (lemma 4) and we now use the lemma to prove a well-known theorem on quadratic forms due to Cochran (1934).

Theorem 4.2.2. Let $\mathbf{x}$ be $\mathscr{N}[\mathbf{0}, \mathbf{I}_n]$ and suppose $\mathbf{A}_1, \mathbf{A}_2, \ldots, \mathbf{A}_m$ is a sequence of $n \times n$ symmetric matrices with ranks $r_1, r_2, \ldots, r_m$ respectively such that $\sum_i \mathbf{A}_i = \mathbf{I}_n$. Then if one (and therefore all) of the conditions of lemma 4.2.1 hold, the quadratic forms $\mathbf{x}'\mathbf{A}_i\mathbf{x}$ are independently distributed as $\chi^2_{r_i}$. (The following proof is due to Dr S.D. Silvey.)

Proof. Since $\mathbf{A}_i$ is symmetric and $\mathbf{A}_i\mathbf{A}_j = \mathbf{0}$ we have that (lemma 1.2.1)

$$R[\mathbf{A}_j] \subset N[\mathbf{A}_i] = \{R[\mathbf{A}_i]\}^{\perp}.$$

Hence $R[\mathbf{A}_1]$, $R[\mathbf{A}_2]$, ..., $R[\mathbf{A}_m]$ are mutually orthogonal spaces and as $\mathbf{I}_n\mathbf{x} = \Sigma \mathbf{A}_i \mathbf{x}$ for every $\mathbf{x}$, their direct sum is E_n. We can therefore construct an orthonormal basis $\mathbf{t}_1, \mathbf{t}_2, \ldots, \mathbf{t}_n$ of E_n such that $\mathbf{t}_1, \mathbf{t}_2, \ldots, \mathbf{t}_{r_1}$ form a basis of $R[\mathbf{A}_1]$; $\mathbf{t}_{r_1+1}, \ldots, \mathbf{t}_{r_1+r_2}$ a basis of $R[\mathbf{A}_2]$, etc. Let $\mathbf{T} = (\mathbf{t}_1, \mathbf{t}_2, \ldots, \mathbf{t}_n)$, then $\mathbf{T}'\mathbf{T} = \mathbf{I}_n$. Now as $\mathbf{A}_1$ is symmetric and idempotent, it represents an orthogonal projection of E_n on $R[\mathbf{A}_1]$ (lemma 3.3.1). Hence $\mathbf{A}_1\mathbf{T} = (\mathbf{t}_1, \mathbf{t}_2, \ldots, \mathbf{t}_{r_1}, \mathbf{0}, \ldots, \mathbf{0})$ and

$$\mathbf{T}'\mathbf{A}_1\mathbf{T} = \begin{bmatrix} \mathbf{I}_{r_1}, & \mathbf{0} \\ \mathbf{0}, & \mathbf{0} \end{bmatrix}.$$

Also we have

$$\mathbf{T}'\mathbf{A}_2\mathbf{T} = \begin{bmatrix} \mathbf{0} & \mathbf{0} & \mathbf{0} \\ \mathbf{0} & \mathbf{I}_{r_2} & \mathbf{0} \\ \mathbf{0} & \mathbf{0} & \mathbf{0} \end{bmatrix} \text{ etc.}$$

Transforming $\mathbf{x} = \mathbf{T}\mathbf{z}$ gives

$$\begin{aligned} \mathbf{x}'\mathbf{A}_1\mathbf{x} &= \mathbf{z}'\mathbf{T}'\mathbf{A}_1\mathbf{T}\mathbf{z} = z_1^2 + \ldots + z_{r_1}^2 \\ \mathbf{x}'\mathbf{A}_2\mathbf{x} &= z_{r_1+1}^2 + \ldots + z_{r_1+r_2}^2, \quad \text{etc.} \end{aligned} \tag{4.2.1}$$

Now $\mathbf{z}$ is $\mathscr{N}[\boldsymbol{\theta}, \mathbf{I}_n]$ (exercise 4, §1.7) and therefore the quadratic forms $\mathbf{x}'\mathbf{A}_i\mathbf{x}$ are independently distributed as $\chi^2_{r_i}$. This completes the proof.

Corollary. The above theorem readily generalises to the case when $\mathbf{x}$ is $\mathscr{N}[\boldsymbol{\theta}, \sigma^2\mathbf{I}_n]$. From equation (4.2.1) it follows that the quadratic forms $\mathbf{x}'\mathbf{A}_i\mathbf{x}/\sigma^2$ are independently distributed as non-central chi-squared with r_i degrees of freedom and non-centrality parameters $\boldsymbol{\theta}'\mathbf{A}_i\boldsymbol{\theta}/\sigma^2$ (lemma 1.9.1).

We now use this theorem to find the distribution of F. Consider the identity

$$\mathbf{I}_n = (\mathbf{I}_n - \mathbf{P}_0) + (\mathbf{P}_0 - \mathbf{P}_1) + \mathbf{P}_1.$$

Then since $\mathbf{P}_0\mathbf{P}_1 = \mathbf{P}_1\mathbf{P}_0$ we have that $\mathbf{I}_n - \mathbf{P}_0$ and $\mathbf{P}_0 - \mathbf{P}_1$ are idempotent and the conditions of lemma 4.2.1 are satisfied. As rank$[\mathbf{I}_n - \mathbf{P}_0]$ $= n - p$ (lemma 3.3.1), it follows that

$$n = n - p + \text{rank}[\mathbf{P}_0 - \mathbf{P}_1] + p - q$$

and therefore rank$[\mathbf{P}_0 - \mathbf{P}_1] = q$. Thus from the corollary above, $\mathbf{y}'(\mathbf{I}_n - \mathbf{P}_0)\mathbf{y}/\sigma^2$ is χ^2_{n-p} with non-centrality parameter $\boldsymbol{\theta}'(\mathbf{I}_n - \mathbf{P}_0)\boldsymbol{\theta}/\sigma^2$ $= 0$ and $\mathbf{y}'(\mathbf{P}_0 - \mathbf{P}_1)\mathbf{y}/\sigma^2$ is $\chi^2_{q,\delta}$ with non-centrality parameter $\delta = \boldsymbol{\theta}'(\mathbf{P}_0 - \mathbf{P}_1)\boldsymbol{\theta}/\sigma^2$. When H is true, $\delta = 0$, and F has the $F_{q,n-p}$ distribution, while if H is false then F has a non-central distribution $F_{q,n-p,\delta}$ (cf. §1.10).

The arithmetic for calculating F is usually set out in the form of an analysis of variance table:

Source	s.s.	d.f.	m.s.s.	E(m.s.s.)
H	$Q_1 - Q_0$	q	$(Q_1 - Q_0)/q$	$\sigma^2 + \delta\sigma^2/q$
Residual	Q_0	$n - p$	$Q_0/(n-p)$	σ^2
Total	Q_1	$n - p + q$		

The fifth column, which gives the expected values of the mean sums of squares (m.s.s.), follows from equation (1.8.3). We note that F is roughly $1 + \delta/q$, and so we would reject H if F is much greater than unity and accept H with confidence if $F \simeq 1$. In fact, we reject H at the $100\alpha\%$ level if $F > F_\alpha$, where F_α is determined by

$$\Pr[F_{q,n-p} \leqslant F_\alpha] = 1 - \alpha .$$

Example. Consider the problem of §2.2 where we considered testing the hypothesis that the means of two populations are equal. Our model is

$$E[y_{ij}] = \theta_i = \mu + \alpha_i \quad \text{for } i = 1, 2;\ j = 1, 2, \ldots, t,$$

and $\alpha_1 + \alpha_2 = 0$. To find the least squares estimate under G, we minimise $\sum_i \sum_j (y_{ij} - \mu - \alpha_i)^2$ subject to $\alpha_1 + \alpha_2 = 0$. Since this condition is sufficient for identifiability, we know from theorem (3.4.1) that the Lagrange multiplier is zero. Thus the least squares estimates are $\mu_0 = \bar{y}_{..}$, $\alpha_{i0} = \bar{y}_{i.} - \bar{y}_{..}$, and the residual s.s. is $Q_0 = \sum_i \sum_j (y_{ij} - \bar{y}_{i.})^2$. To find the least squares estimates under $H: \alpha_1 = \alpha_2 = 0$, we minimise $\sum_i \sum_j (y_{ij} - \mu)^2$ giving $\mu_1 = \bar{y}_{..}$ as before. The test s.s. is given by

$$\begin{aligned} Q_1 - Q_0 &= t\sum_i (\bar{y}_{i.} - \bar{y}_{..})^2 \\ &= t\sum_i \alpha_{i0}^2, \end{aligned}$$

and since α_{i0} is the same function of the y_{ij} as α_i is of the θ_{ij}, the non-centrality parameter is simply $t\sum_i \alpha_i^2/\sigma^2 = \frac{1}{2}t(\theta_1 - \theta_2)^2/\sigma^2$. The F-test statistic is

$$(2t-2)\,t\sum_i (\bar{y}_{i.} - \bar{y}_{..})^2 / \sum_i \sum_j (y_{ij} - \bar{y}_{i.})^2$$

and is distributed as $F_{1,2t-2}$ when H is true.

4.3 A canonical form

Any linear hypothesis H can be reduced – by a suitable transformation on the sample space of $\mathbf{y}$ – to the canonical form $\mathbf{z} = \boldsymbol{\mu} + \mathbf{e}$ with

$$G : \mu_{p+1} = \dots = \mu_n = 0 \quad \text{and}$$
$$H : \mu_1 = \mu_2 = \dots = \mu_q = \mu_{p+1} = \dots = \mu_n = 0.$$

The transformation which achieves this is $\mathbf{y} = \mathbf{T}\mathbf{z}$, $\boldsymbol{\theta} = \mathbf{T}\boldsymbol{\mu}$, where $\mathbf{T}$ is the orthogonal matrix defined in the proof of theorem 4.2.2. By choosing $\mathbf{A}_1 = (\mathbf{P}_0 - \mathbf{P}_1)$ and $\mathbf{A}_2 = \mathbf{I} - \mathbf{P}_0$ we have

$$\mathbf{y}'(\mathbf{P}_0 - \mathbf{P}_1)\mathbf{y} = z_1^2 + \dots + z_q^2$$

and

$$\mathbf{y}'(\mathbf{I} - \mathbf{P}_0)\mathbf{y} = z_{p+1}^2 + \dots + z_n^2.$$

The non-centrality parameter for Q_0/σ^2 is $(\mu_{p+1}^2 + \dots + \mu_n^2)/\sigma^2$ which is zero if and only if $\mu_{p+1} = \dots = \mu_n = 0$. Similarly H is true if and only if $\mu_1 = \dots = \mu_q = 0$ as well.

4.4 The Wald principle

In this section we show that the F test is not only based on the likelihood ratio principle but is also the test statistic obtained by applying a general principle due to Wald. We shall require the following lemmas.

Lemma 4.4.1. $\omega^\perp \cap \Omega = R[\mathbf{P}_0 - \mathbf{P}_1]$.

Proof. Any vector $\boldsymbol{\theta} \in \Omega$ takes the form (lemma 3.3.1)

$$\boldsymbol{\theta} = \mathbf{P}_0\boldsymbol{\alpha} = (\mathbf{P}_0 - \mathbf{P}_1)\boldsymbol{\alpha} + \mathbf{P}_1\boldsymbol{\alpha}$$

for some $\boldsymbol{\alpha}$. We thus have an orthogonal decomposition of $\boldsymbol{\theta}$ corresponding to $\Omega = \omega^\perp \cap \Omega \oplus \omega$, and $\mathbf{P}_0 - \mathbf{P}_1$ represents the projection of E_n on $\omega^\perp \cap \Omega$. The result follows from lemma 3.3.1.

Lemma 4.4.2. If $\mathbf{A}_1$ is any matrix such that

$$\omega = \Omega \cap N[\mathbf{A}_1] \quad \text{then} \quad \omega^\perp \cap \Omega = R[\mathbf{P}_0\mathbf{A}_1'].$$

Proof. From lemma 1.4.1,

$$\begin{aligned}\omega^\perp \cap \Omega &= [\Omega \cap N[\mathbf{A}_1]]^\perp \cap \Omega \\ &= [\Omega^\perp + R[\mathbf{A}_1']] \cap \Omega.\end{aligned}$$

If $\boldsymbol{\theta}$ belongs to the right-hand side of the above equation, then $\mathbf{P}_0\boldsymbol{\theta} = \boldsymbol{\theta}$ and $\boldsymbol{\theta} = (\mathbf{I} - \mathbf{P}_0)\boldsymbol{\alpha} + \mathbf{A}_1'\boldsymbol{\beta}$ for some $\boldsymbol{\alpha}$ and $\boldsymbol{\beta}$; therefore $\boldsymbol{\theta} = \mathbf{P}_0\mathbf{A}_1'\boldsymbol{\beta} \in R[\mathbf{P}_0\mathbf{A}_1']$. In a similar manner we can show that if $\boldsymbol{\theta} \in R[\mathbf{P}_0\mathbf{A}_1']$ then $\boldsymbol{\theta} \in \omega^\perp \cap \Omega$. Thus

$$[\Omega^\perp + R[\mathbf{A}_1']] \cap \Omega = R[\mathbf{P}_0\mathbf{A}_1'] \tag{4.4.1}$$

and the lemma is proved.

Lemma 4.4.3. If $\mathbf{A}_1$ is a $q \times n$ matrix of rank q, then $\text{rank}[\mathbf{P}_0\mathbf{A}_1'] = q$ if and only if $R[\mathbf{A}_1'] \cap \Omega^\perp = \mathbf{0}$.

Proof. Let the rows of $\mathbf{A}_1$ be $\mathbf{a}_{1i}'(i=1,2,\dots,q)$. If $\text{rank}[\mathbf{P}_0\mathbf{A}_1'] \neq q$, then the columns of $\mathbf{P}_0\mathbf{A}_1'$ are linearly dependent, that is there exist $c_1, c_2, \ldots, c_q$ not all zero such that $\sum_i c_i \mathbf{P}_0 \mathbf{a}_{1i} = \mathbf{0}$. This implies that there exists a vector $\sum_i c_i \mathbf{a}_{1i} \in R[\mathbf{A}_1']$ which is perpendicular to Ω and therefore $R[\mathbf{A}_1'] \cap \Omega^{\perp} \neq \mathbf{0}$. The proof of the lemma follows.

Suppose we choose $\mathbf{A}_1$ such that $N[\mathbf{A}_1] = \omega \oplus \Omega^{\perp}$, then, using a similar argument to that which led to equation (4.4.1), $\omega = \Omega \cap N[\mathbf{A}_1]$ and by lemma 4.4.2, $\mathbf{P}_0 - \mathbf{P}_1$ represents the projection onto $R[\mathbf{P}_0\mathbf{A}_1']$. But by lemmas 1.2.1 and 1.4.1

$$\begin{aligned} R[\mathbf{A}_1'] \cap \Omega^{\perp} &= [\omega \oplus \Omega^{\perp}]^{\perp} \cap \Omega^{\perp} \\ &= \omega^{\perp} \cap \Omega \cap \Omega^{\perp} \\ &= \mathbf{0}. \end{aligned}$$

Therefore by lemma 4.4.3, $\mathbf{P}_0\mathbf{A}_1'$ has rank q, $\mathbf{A}_1\mathbf{P}_0\mathbf{A}_1'$ is non-singular, and from example 1 (§3.4)

$$\mathbf{y}'(\mathbf{P}_0 - \mathbf{P}_1)\mathbf{y} = \mathbf{y}'\mathbf{P}_0\mathbf{A}_1'(\mathbf{A}_1\mathbf{P}_0\mathbf{A}_1')^{-1}\mathbf{A}_1\mathbf{P}_0\mathbf{y} \tag{4.4.2}$$

$$= (\mathbf{A}_1\boldsymbol{\theta}_0)'(\mathbf{A}_1\mathbf{P}_0\mathbf{A}_1')^{-1}\mathbf{A}_1\boldsymbol{\theta}_0. \tag{4.4.3}$$

The dispersion matrix of $\mathbf{A}_1\boldsymbol{\theta}_0$ is $\mathbf{D} = \mathbf{A}_1\mathbf{P}_0\mathbf{A}_1'\sigma^2$, and if $\mathbf{D}_0$ is its value for $\sigma^2 = \sigma_0^2$, the maximum likelihood estimate of σ^2, then

$$F = (n-p)(\mathbf{A}_1\theta_0)'\mathbf{D}_0^{-1}(\mathbf{A}_1\theta_0)/nq.$$

Thus to test whether $\mathbf{A}_1\boldsymbol{\theta} = \mathbf{0}$ we replace $\boldsymbol{\theta}$ by its maximum likelihood estimate and see if $\mathbf{A}_1\boldsymbol{\theta}_0$ is "near enough" to zero by calculating F, a simple positive semi-definite quadratic function of $\mathbf{A}_1\boldsymbol{\theta}_0$. This simple test principle, due to Wald (1943), is discussed further in Chapter 11.

Example. Consider a regression model with $\Omega = R[\mathbf{X}]$ and $\omega = R[\mathbf{X}_p]$, where $\mathbf{X}$ is $n \times r$ and of rank r, and $\mathbf{X}_p$ consists of the first p columns of $\mathbf{X}$. Then from Example 1, §3.4,

$$\mathbf{P}_0 = \mathbf{X}(\mathbf{X}'\mathbf{X})^{-1}\mathbf{X}', \quad \mathbf{P}_1 = \mathbf{X}_p(\mathbf{X}_p'\mathbf{X}_p)^{-1}\mathbf{X}_p',$$

and we can immediately write down our F statistic. However, using the Wald principle, we can express $\mathbf{P}_0 - \mathbf{P}_1$ as a single matrix as follows. We first of all show that if $\mathbf{X} = (\mathbf{X}_p, \mathbf{X}_{r-p})$ then

$$\omega = \Omega \cap N[\mathbf{X}_{r-p}'(\mathbf{I} - \mathbf{P}_1)]. \tag{4.4.4}$$

If $\boldsymbol{\theta} \in \omega$ then $\boldsymbol{\theta} \in \Omega$, $(\mathbf{I} - \mathbf{P}_1)\boldsymbol{\theta} = \mathbf{0}$ and $\boldsymbol{\theta}$ belongs to the right-hand side of equation (4.4.4). Conversely, if $\boldsymbol{\theta}$ belongs to the right-hand side, then $\boldsymbol{\theta} = \mathbf{X}_p\boldsymbol{\beta}_p + \mathbf{X}_{r-p}\boldsymbol{\beta}_{r-p}$ and $\mathbf{X}_{r-p}'(\mathbf{I} - \mathbf{P}_1)\boldsymbol{\theta} = 0$. Thus

$$\mathbf{X}_{r-p}'(\mathbf{I} - \mathbf{P}_1)\mathbf{X}_{r-p}\boldsymbol{\beta}_{r-p} = 0$$

and by lemma 4.4.3 the above matrix is non-singular – as $R[\mathbf{X}_{r-p}] \cap \omega =$

0 – giving $\boldsymbol{\beta}_{r-p} = \mathbf{0}$. Hence $\boldsymbol{\theta} \in R[\mathbf{X}_p] = \omega$ and equation (4.4.4) is established. Since $\mathbf{P}_0 \mathbf{X}_{r-p} = \mathbf{X}_{r-p}$,

$$\mathbf{P}_0(\mathbf{I} - \mathbf{P}_1)\mathbf{X}_{r-p} = (\mathbf{I} - \mathbf{P}_1)\mathbf{X}_{r-p}$$

and it follows from equation (4.4.2) that

$$\mathbf{P}_0 - \mathbf{P}_1 = (\mathbf{I} - \mathbf{P}_1)\mathbf{X}_{r-p}\{\mathbf{X}'_{r-p}(\mathbf{I} - \mathbf{P}_1)\mathbf{X}_{r-p}\}^{-1}\mathbf{X}'_{r-p}(\mathbf{I} - \mathbf{P}_1).$$

Other examples demonstrating this Wald approach are given in Seber (1964a).

4.5 Contrasts

A contrast of the vector $\boldsymbol{\theta}$ is any linear function $\mathbf{c}'\boldsymbol{\theta}$ such that $\sum_i c_i = 0$. Two contrasts $\mathbf{c}'\boldsymbol{\theta}$ and $\mathbf{d}'\boldsymbol{\theta}$ are said to be orthogonal if $\mathbf{c}'\mathbf{d} = 0$. For example, $\theta_1 - \theta_2$ and $\theta_1 + \theta_2 + \theta_3 - 3\theta_4$ are two orthogonal contrasts, and in § 2.2 where we considered the hypothesis that the means of two populations are the same, the linear functions $\mathbf{C}\boldsymbol{\theta}$ are also contrasts of $\boldsymbol{\theta}$.

The situation that we often meet in factorial experiments is that we are given a set of independent contrasts $\mathbf{a}'_i\boldsymbol{\theta}$ $(i = 1, 2, \ldots, n-p)$ equal to zero and we wish to test whether a further set of q orthogonal contrasts $\mathbf{a}'_{1i}\boldsymbol{\theta}$ $(i = 1, 2, \ldots, q)$, which are orthogonal to the previous set, are also zero. If we put $\mathbf{A} = (\mathbf{a}_1, \ldots, \mathbf{a}_{n-p})'$ and $\mathbf{A}_1 = (\mathbf{a}_{11}, \ldots, \mathbf{a}_{1q})'$ then G is $\mathbf{A}\boldsymbol{\theta} = \mathbf{0}$ and H is $\mathbf{A}\boldsymbol{\theta} = \mathbf{0}$, $\mathbf{A}_1\boldsymbol{\theta} = \mathbf{0}$ where $\mathbf{A}\mathbf{A}'_1 = \mathbf{0}$, and $\mathbf{A}_1\mathbf{A}'_1$ is diagonal. Define $d_i(\boldsymbol{\theta}) = \|\mathbf{a}_{1i}\|^{-1}\mathbf{a}'_{1i}\boldsymbol{\theta}$ $(i = 1, 2, \ldots, q)$, a set of orthonormal contrasts. Since $\mathbf{P}_0 = \mathbf{I} - \mathbf{A}'(\mathbf{A}\mathbf{A}')^{-1}\mathbf{A}$ (example 3, § 3.4) it follows from equation (4.4.3) that

$$F = \frac{n-p}{q} \frac{\sum_{i=1}^{q} d_i^2(\boldsymbol{\theta}_0)}{\mathbf{y}'(\mathbf{I} - \mathbf{P}_0)\mathbf{y}}$$

EXERCISE 7. Prove that any linear hypothesis can be reduced to the canonical form $\Omega : \mathbf{C}\boldsymbol{\theta} = \mathbf{0}$, $\omega : \mathbf{C}\boldsymbol{\theta} = \mathbf{0}$, $\mathbf{C}_1\boldsymbol{\theta} = \mathbf{0}$, where $\mathbf{C}\mathbf{C}' = \mathbf{I}$, $\mathbf{C}_1\mathbf{C}'_1 = \mathbf{I}$, and $\mathbf{C}\mathbf{C}'_1 = \mathbf{0}$.

Example (Kempthorne, 1952, Chapter 13). Consider a factorial experiment with two factors a and b each at two levels a_1, a_2 and b_1, b_2. Then the yields from the four treatment combinations in the experiment may be represented as $a_2b_2, a_2b_1, a_1b_2, a_1b_1$. Now we have

$$\text{effect of } a \text{ at level } b_1 = a_2b_1 - a_1b_1$$

$$\text{effect of } a \text{ at level } b_2 = a_2b_2 - a_1b_2$$

and the average effect A is given by

$$A = \tfrac{1}{2}(a_2b_2 - a_1b_2 + a_2b_1 - a_1b_1).$$

If the two factors were acting independently we would expect the two effects at levels b_1 and b_2 to be equal, but in general they will be different, and their difference is a measure of the extent to which the factors interact. We define the interaction AB to be half the difference between these two effects; thus:

$$AB = \frac{1}{2}(a_2b_2 - a_1b_2 - a_2b_1 + a_1b_1).$$

In a similar manner we can define the average effect of b as

$$B = \frac{1}{2}(a_2b_2 - a_2b_1 + a_1b_2 - a_1b_1),$$

and BA is half the difference of the two effects of b. However, $AB = BA$ and the concept of interaction is a symmetrical one as one would expect. We note that A, B and AB are three orthonormal contrasts of the four treatments, and denoting the mean yield by M we have the orthogonal transformation

$$\begin{bmatrix} 2M \\ A \\ B \\ AB \end{bmatrix} = \frac{1}{2}\begin{bmatrix} 1 & 1 & 1 & 1 \\ 1 & 1 & -1 & -1 \\ 1 & -1 & 1 & -1 \\ 1 & -1 & -1 & 1 \end{bmatrix}\begin{bmatrix} a_2b_2 \\ a_2b_1 \\ a_1b_2 \\ a_1b_1 \end{bmatrix}.$$

We now denote the four yields a_ib_j by θ_1, θ_2, θ_3 and θ_4 respectively and suppose we have t observations on each yield θ_i. Then the hypothesis of interest, H, is that the four population means θ_i are equal (cf. § 2.2). If y_{ij} is the jth observation on the ith mean ($i = 1, \ldots, 4$; $j = 1, 2, \ldots, t$), then we assume the model $y_{ij} = \theta_{ij} + e_{ij}$ and $G : \theta_{ij} = \theta_i$. If $\boldsymbol{\theta}$ is the vector with elements θ_{ij} then G states that certain contrasts $\theta_{ij} - \bar{\theta}_{i.}$ of $\boldsymbol{\theta}$ are zero and H is equivalent to $A = B = AB = 0$, where A, B, AB are orthogonal contrasts in $\boldsymbol{\theta}$. For example

$$\begin{aligned} 2A(\boldsymbol{\theta}) &= a_2b_2 + a_2b_1 - a_1b_2 - a_1b_1 \\ &= \theta_1 + \theta_2 - \theta_3 - \theta_4 \\ &= \bar{\theta}_{1.} + \bar{\theta}_{2.} - \bar{\theta}_{3.} - \bar{\theta}_{4.} \end{aligned}$$

and this is a contrast in $\boldsymbol{\theta}$ since $\theta_{1j} + \theta_{2j} - \theta_{3j} - \theta_{4j}$ is a contrast and a sum of contrasts is still a contrast. Also the two sets of contrasts for G and H are orthogonal, and therefore the general theory described above can be applied to this example. All we require is $\boldsymbol{\theta}_0$, and our F statistic for testing H is

$$F = \frac{4(t-1)t}{3} \; \frac{A(\boldsymbol{\theta}_0)^2 + B(\boldsymbol{\theta}_0)^2 + AB(\boldsymbol{\theta}_0)^2}{\|\mathbf{y} - \boldsymbol{\theta}_0\|^2}$$

Minimising $\sum_i \sum_j (y_{ij} - \theta_i)^2$ gives $\theta_{i0} = \bar{y}_{i.}$, the least squares estimate of θ_i. Hence

$$2A(\boldsymbol{\theta}_0) = \bar{y}_{1.} + \bar{y}_{2.} - \bar{y}_{3.} - \bar{y}_{4.} \quad \text{etc.}$$

and

$$\| \mathbf{y} - \boldsymbol{\theta}_0 \|^2 = \sum_i \sum_j (y_{ij} - \bar{y}_{i.})^2$$

EXERCISE 8. Using the above orthogonal transformation prove that $A(\boldsymbol{\theta}_0)^2 + B(\boldsymbol{\theta}_0)^2 + AB(\boldsymbol{\theta}_0)^2 = \sum_i (\bar{y}_{i.} - \bar{y}_{..})^2$.

4.6 Confidence regions

In most practical applications of linear hypothesis theory our prime interest is not just in significant tests but also in the finding of confidence regions and confidence intervals for the unknown parameters.

Suppose we are given $G : \mathbf{A}\boldsymbol{\theta} = \mathbf{0}$ and we wish to test $H : \mathbf{A}\boldsymbol{\theta} = \mathbf{0}$, $\mathbf{A}_1\boldsymbol{\theta} = \mathbf{0}$; then, from equation (4.4.2),

$$F = (\mathbf{A}_1\boldsymbol{\theta}_0)'(\mathbf{A}_1\mathbf{P}_0\mathbf{A}_1')^{-1}\mathbf{A}_1\boldsymbol{\theta}_0/qs^2.$$

Now $\mathbf{A}_1\boldsymbol{\theta}_0$ is $\mathscr{N}[\mathbf{A}_1\boldsymbol{\theta}, \sigma^2\mathbf{B}]$, where $\mathbf{B} = \mathbf{A}_1\mathbf{P}_0\mathbf{A}_1'$, and therefore

$$F_{q,\,n-p} = (\mathbf{A}_1\boldsymbol{\theta}_0 - \mathbf{A}_1\boldsymbol{\theta})'\mathbf{B}^{-1}(\mathbf{A}_1\boldsymbol{\theta}_0 - \mathbf{A}_1\boldsymbol{\theta})/qs^2$$

has the central F distribution when G is true.

If $\Pr[F_{q,\,n-p} \leqslant F_{q,\,n-p}(\alpha)] = 1 - \alpha$, then a $100(1-\alpha)$ per cent confidence region for $\mathbf{A}_1\boldsymbol{\theta}$ is given by

$$(\mathbf{A}_1\boldsymbol{\theta}_0 - \mathbf{A}_1\boldsymbol{\theta})'\mathbf{B}^{-1}(\mathbf{A}_1\boldsymbol{\theta}_0 - \mathbf{A}_1\boldsymbol{\theta}) \leqslant qs^2F_{q,\,n-p}(\alpha).$$

If we wanted to obtain a confidence interval for a single constraint $\psi = \mathbf{a}'\boldsymbol{\theta}$, then by the Gauss–Markov theorem (3.5.1)

$$\psi_0 = \mathbf{a}'\boldsymbol{\theta}_0 = \mathbf{a}'\mathbf{P}_0\mathbf{y} = \mathbf{a}_0'\mathbf{y}, \quad \text{say}$$

and the confidence interval for ψ is

$$(\mathbf{a}_0'\mathbf{a}_0)^{-1}(\psi_0 - \psi)^2 \leqslant s^2F_{1,\,n-p}(\alpha).$$

As $F_{1,\,n-p}$ is t_{n-p}^2, where t_{n-p} is the t distribution with $n-p$ degrees of freedom, this confidence interval can also be expressed in the form

$$\psi_0 - s\,\|\mathbf{a}_0\|\,t_{n-p}(\alpha/2) \leqslant \psi \leqslant \psi_0 + s\,\|\mathbf{a}_0\|\,t_{n-p}(\alpha/2).$$

For constructing simultaneous confidence intervals, several so-called multiple comparison methods are available, and a general discussion of these methods is given in Scheffé (1959, Chapter 3) and Dunn (1959).

Confidence intervals for σ^2 can be constructed from $(n-p)s^2/\sigma^2$ which is distributed as χ_{n-p}^2.

4.7 Additional references

For general references on quadratic forms and idempotent matrices cf. Kendall and Stuart (1959) and Graybill (1961).

Lemma 4.2.1 is generalised by Graybill and Marsaglia (1957) and Banerjee (1964) to the case where

$$\sum_{i=1}^{m} \mathbf{A}_i = \mathbf{A}.$$

Hogg and Craig (1958) prove the following useful result. Let Q, Q_1 and Q_2 be quadratic forms in normal variables such that $Q = Q_1 + Q_2$, and Q and Q_1 have non-central chi-squared distributions. Then if $Q_2 \geqslant 0$, i.e. positive semi-definite, Q_1 and Q_2 have independent non-central chi-squared distributions.

Two recent fields of research which may interest the reader are testing linear hypotheses against ordered alternatives (Abelson and Tukey (1963)) and non-parametric tests of linear hypotheses (Lehmann (1964)).

CHAPTER 5

PROPERTIES OF THE F TEST

5.1 Power of the F test

Suppose $\mathbf{y} = \boldsymbol{\theta} + \mathbf{e}$, $G : \boldsymbol{\theta} \in \Omega$, a p-dimensional vector space, and $H : \boldsymbol{\theta} \in \omega$, a $p-q$-dimensional subspace of Ω; $\mathbf{e}$ is $\mathcal{N}[\mathbf{0}, \sigma^2 \mathbf{I}_n]$. To test H we choose a region W called the "critical region" and we reject H if and only if $\mathbf{y} \in W$. The *power* of the test $\beta(W, \boldsymbol{\theta})$ is defined to be the probability of rejecting H when $\boldsymbol{\theta}$ is the true value of $E[\mathbf{y}]$. Thus,

$$\beta(W, \boldsymbol{\theta}) = \Pr[\mathbf{y} \in W \mid \boldsymbol{\theta}]$$

and is a function of W and $\boldsymbol{\theta}$. The *size* of a critical region W is $\sup(\boldsymbol{\theta} \in \omega)\, \beta(W, \boldsymbol{\theta})$, and if $\beta(W, \boldsymbol{\theta}) = \alpha$ for all $\boldsymbol{\theta} \in \omega$ then W is said to be a *similar* region of size α. If W is of size α and $\beta(W, \boldsymbol{\theta}) \geqslant \alpha$ for every $\boldsymbol{\theta} \in \Omega - \omega$ ($\Omega - \omega$ denotes the set of all points in Ω which are not in ω) then W is said to be *unbiased.* In particular, if we have the strict inequality $\beta(W, \boldsymbol{\theta}) > \alpha$ for $\boldsymbol{\theta} \in \Omega - \omega$, then W is said to be *consistent*. Finally we define W to be a uniformly most powerful (U.M.P.) critical region of a given class C if $W \in C$ and if, for any $W' \in C$ and all $\boldsymbol{\theta} \in \Omega - \omega$,

$$\beta(W, \boldsymbol{\theta}) \geqslant \beta(W', \boldsymbol{\theta}).$$

Obviously a wide choice of W is possible for testing H, and so we would endeavour to choose a critical region which has some, or if possible, all of the desired properties mentioned above, namely similarity, unbiasedness or consistency, and uniformly-most-powerfulness for certain reasonable classes of critical regions. The F test for H, given by

$$F = \frac{f_2}{f_1} \frac{\mathbf{y}'(\mathbf{P}_0 - \mathbf{P}_1)\mathbf{y}}{\mathbf{y}'(\mathbf{I} - \mathbf{P}_0)\mathbf{y}}$$

where $f_2 = n - p$ and $f_1 = q$, provides such a critical region W_0, say, and we shall now give the properties of W_0.

We note first of all that W_0 is the set of vectors $\mathbf{y}$ such that $F > F_\alpha$, where

$$\Pr[F > F_\alpha \mid \boldsymbol{\theta} \in \omega] = \alpha$$

and therefore W_0 is a similar region of size α. The similarity property holds because F is distributed as F_{f_1, f_2} when H is true, and therefore it does not depend on $\boldsymbol{\theta}$ when $\boldsymbol{\theta} \in \omega$. The power of W_0 depends on $\boldsymbol{\theta}$ through the non-centrality parameter $\delta = \boldsymbol{\theta}'(\mathbf{P}_0 - \mathbf{P}_1)\boldsymbol{\theta}/\sigma^2$ and is therefore a function of δ and W_0, say $\beta(W_0, \delta)$. Also

$$\beta(W_0, \delta) = \Pr[v > v_\alpha = f_1 F_\alpha / f_1 F_\alpha + f_2]$$

where v has the non-central Beta distribution given in § 1.10, namely

$$\beta(W_0, \delta) = e^{-\delta/2} \sum_{m=0}^{\infty} \frac{(\delta/2)}{m!} \int_{v_\alpha}^{1} \frac{v^{f_1/2 - 1 + m} (1 - v)^{f_2/2 - 1}}{B[\frac{1}{2}f_1 + m, \frac{1}{2}f_2]} dv .$$

It is well known that $\beta(W_0, \delta)$ can be increased by (a) decreasing f_1 keeping f_2 and δ fixed, (b) increasing f_2 keeping f_1 and δ fixed, or (c) increasing δ keeping f_1 and f_2 fixed. Now since $\delta = 0$ if and only if $\boldsymbol{\theta} \in \omega$, and $\beta(W_0, \delta)$ is a monotonic strictly increasing function of δ, then $\beta(W_0, \delta) > \beta(W_0, 0) = \alpha$ when $\boldsymbol{\theta} \in \Omega - \omega$ and W_0 is consistent.

Before turning our attention to the classes of critical regions for which W_0 is U.M.P., we recall from §4.3 that our linear hypothesis can be put in the canonical form

$$\mathbf{z} = \boldsymbol{\mu} + \mathbf{e}, \quad \text{where} \quad \mathbf{e} \text{ is } \mathscr{N}[\mathbf{0}, \sigma^2 \mathbf{I}_n]$$

$$G : \mu_{p+1} = \ldots = \mu_n = 0 \quad \text{and}$$

$$H : \mu_1 = \ldots = \mu_q = \mu_{p+1} = \ldots = \mu_n = 0$$

giving

$$F = \frac{f_2}{f_1} \frac{\sum_{i=1}^{q} z_i^2}{\sum_{i=p+1}^{n} z_i^2}$$

and $\delta = \sum_{i=1}^{q} \mu_i^2/\sigma^2$. From Lehmann (1950, 1959) we have that

(1) W_0 is U.M.P. among all critical regions of size α which are invariant under the transformations

(i) $z_i' = a z_i \quad (i = 1, 2, \ldots, n;\ a > 0)$;

(ii) $z_i' = z_i + b_i \quad (i = q+1, \ldots, p;\ -\infty < b_i < \infty)$;

(iii) orthogonal transformations on $z_{p+1}, \ldots, z_n$;

(iv) orthogonal transformations on $z_1, \ldots, z_q$.

This restriction to invariant tests is a very reasonable one as the canonical forms of H and F are invariant under the above transformations. In terms of the original variables $\mathbf{y}$, the above transformations are equivalent to

(i)′ $\quad \mathbf{x} = a\mathbf{y} \quad (a > 0);$

(ii)′ $\quad \mathbf{x} = \mathbf{y} + \boldsymbol{\phi} \quad (\boldsymbol{\phi} \in \omega);$

(iii)′ and (iv)′ : orthogonal transformations of the form $\mathbf{x} = \mathbf{T}_i\mathbf{y}$ $(i = 1, 2)$ where $\mathbf{T}_1\mathbf{P}_0 = \mathbf{P}_0$, $\mathbf{T}_2\mathbf{P}_1 = \mathbf{P}_1$ and $\mathbf{T}_2(\mathbf{I} - \mathbf{P}_0) = \mathbf{I} - \mathbf{P}_0$.

To show that (iii)′ and (iv)′ are equivalent to (iii) and (iv), consider

$$\begin{aligned}\mathbf{T}_1\mathbf{y} &= \mathbf{T}_1\mathbf{P}_0\mathbf{y} + \mathbf{T}_1(\mathbf{I} - \mathbf{P}_0)\mathbf{y} \\ &= \mathbf{P}_0\mathbf{y} + \mathbf{T}_1(\mathbf{I} - \mathbf{P}_0)\mathbf{y}\end{aligned}$$

and

$$\begin{aligned}\mathbf{T}_2\mathbf{y} &= \mathbf{T}_2\mathbf{P}_1\mathbf{y} + \mathbf{T}_2(\mathbf{P}_0 - \mathbf{P}_1)\mathbf{y} + \mathbf{T}_2(\mathbf{I} - \mathbf{P}_0)\mathbf{y} \\ &= \mathbf{P}_1\mathbf{y} + \mathbf{T}_2(\mathbf{P}_0 - \mathbf{P}_1)\mathbf{y} + (\mathbf{I} - \mathbf{P}_0)\mathbf{y}.\end{aligned}$$

As an orthogonal matrix represents a rotational transformation we see that $\mathbf{T}_1$ and $\mathbf{T}_2$ only rotate the components $(\mathbf{I} - \mathbf{P}_0)\mathbf{y}$ and $(\mathbf{P}_0 - \mathbf{P}_1)\mathbf{y}$ of $\mathbf{y}$ respectively and leave the remaining components in each of the above decompositions unchanged. Hence $\mathbf{T}_1$ and $\mathbf{T}_2$ represent orthogonal transformations on $\Omega^{\perp}$ and $\omega^{\perp} \cap \Omega$ respectively and (iii)′, (iv)′ are equivalent to (iii), (iv).

EXERCISE 9. Prove that F is invariant under the above transformations on $\mathbf{y}$.

Wolfowitz (1949) proves the following three properties of the F-test:

(2) in the class of all similar regions of size α, W_0 maximises the integral of its power on the surface $S = \{\boldsymbol{\theta} : \boldsymbol{\theta}'(\mathbf{P}_0 - \mathbf{P}_1)\boldsymbol{\theta} = d\}$ for all positive d, that is

$$\int_S \beta(W, \boldsymbol{\theta})\, ds \Big/ \int_S ds$$

is a maximum when $W = W_0$ (Wald, 1942); here ds is an element of surface,

(3) (a consequence of (2)) W_0 is U.M.P. among all critical regions of size α which have the property that their power depends on $\boldsymbol{\theta}$ only through δ (Hsu, 1941b),

(4) W_0 is the most stringent test of size α (Lehmann, 1950, 1959).

From a lemma due to Hunt and Stein, Lehmann (1950) proves that

(5) for tests of size α, W_0 minimises the maximum expected loss with respect to any invariant loss function; or in terms of power, it maximises the minimum power over any invariant class of alternatives. For

example, W_0 maximises the minimum power over the contour $\boldsymbol{\theta}'(\mathbf{P}_0 - \mathbf{P}_1)\boldsymbol{\theta} = d$ (Kiefer 1958, p. 680). This minimax property is a consequence of the existence of a U.M.P. invariant test. For a further discussion of the above properties of the F test the reader is referred to Scheffé (1959, Chapter 2), Plackett (1960a, Chapter 4) and Lehmann (1959, Chapter 7).

Another property of W_0 has been proved recently by Saw (1964) who shows that

(6) W_0 is U.M.P. among the class C of all consistent, variance ratio type tests. A variance ratio test is a test of the form $s\,\mathbf{y}'\mathbf{A}_r\mathbf{y}/r\mathbf{y}'\mathbf{B}_s\mathbf{y}$ where the numerator and denominator s.s. are distributed independently as σ^2 times a non-central chi-squared distribution with r and s degrees of freedom respectively. Also the non-centrality parameter $\boldsymbol{\theta}'\mathbf{B}_s\boldsymbol{\theta}/\sigma^2$, for the error s.s., $\mathbf{y}'\mathbf{B}_s\mathbf{y}$, is zero when $\boldsymbol{\theta} \in \Omega$, and the non-centrality parameter of the hypothesis s.s., $\mathbf{y}'\mathbf{A}_r\mathbf{y}$, is zero when $\boldsymbol{\theta} \in \omega$. For a consistent test we must have $\boldsymbol{\theta}'\mathbf{A}_r\boldsymbol{\theta} > 0$ when $\boldsymbol{\theta} \in \Omega - \omega$. We now give Saw's proof for the property (6) as it is a good example of the vector space approach.

The quadratic $\mathbf{y}'\mathbf{B}_s\mathbf{y}$ is distributed as $\sigma^2\chi_s^2$ if and only if $\mathbf{B}_s$ is symmetric and idempotent (lemma 1.9.1), and therefore $\mathbf{B}_s$ represents an orthogonal projection of E_n on some vector space B_s of dimension s. The non-centrality parameter of $\mathbf{y}'\mathbf{B}_s\mathbf{y}$ is, in units of $1/\sigma^2$, the square of the distance from the origin to the projection of $\boldsymbol{\theta}$ on B_s, i.e. $\boldsymbol{\theta}'\mathbf{B}_s\boldsymbol{\theta}$. If this is to be zero for every $\boldsymbol{\theta} \in \Omega$ then $B_s \perp \Omega$, so that $s \leqslant n-p$. When $s = n-p$ there is a unique vector space B_s, namely $\Omega^\perp$, and therefore $\mathbf{y}'(\mathbf{I}-\mathbf{P}_0)\mathbf{y}$ is the unique error s.s. with maximum degrees of freedom $n-p$. If $\mathbf{y}'\mathbf{A}_r\mathbf{y}$ is $\sigma^2\chi_r^2$ then $\mathbf{A}_r$ represents an orthogonal projection on some vector space A_r of dimension r. Since $\mathbf{y}'\mathbf{A}_r\mathbf{y}$ and $\mathbf{y}'\mathbf{B}_s\mathbf{y}$ are independent then $\mathbf{A}_r\mathbf{B}_s = \mathbf{0}$ (lemma 1.9.2) or geometrically $A_r \perp B_s$. As $\mathbf{y}'\mathbf{A}_r\mathbf{y}$ has zero non-centrality parameter when $\boldsymbol{\theta} \in \omega$, then $A_r \perp \omega$. Thus $A_r \subset \omega^\perp \cap \Omega \oplus B_s^\perp \cap \Omega^\perp = D$, say, and we now show that for a consistent test, $r \geqslant \dim[\omega^\perp \cap \Omega] = q$.

Suppose that $r < q$ and let A_r^* be the projection of A_r on $\omega^\perp \cap \Omega$. If $\boldsymbol{\theta}$ is any point in $\omega^\perp \cap \Omega$ such that $\boldsymbol{\theta} \perp A_r^*$, then $\mathbf{A}_r\boldsymbol{\theta}$ — the projection of $\boldsymbol{\theta}$ on A_r — is zero; that is, $\boldsymbol{\theta}'\mathbf{A}_r\boldsymbol{\theta} = 0$. Such a $\boldsymbol{\theta}$ exists since $r < q$ and this contradicts the requirement of consistency. Hence we may assume that $r \geqslant q$.

If $B_s = \Omega^\perp$ then for a consistent test we must have $A_r = \omega^\perp \cap \Omega$ and $\mathbf{y}'\mathbf{A}_r\mathbf{y}$ $(= \mathbf{y}'(\mathbf{P}_0 - \mathbf{P}_1)\mathbf{y})$ is the unique hypothesis s.s. with minimum degrees of freedom q. For a general variance ratio test, however, when $B_s \subset \Omega^\perp$, $A_r \neq \omega^\perp \cap \Omega$. Since $D \supset A_r$, $\mathbf{P}_D\mathbf{A}_r = \mathbf{A}_r$, where $\mathbf{P}_D$ is the projection matrix on D. Thus for every $\boldsymbol{\theta} \in \Omega - \omega$

$$\begin{aligned} \|(\mathbf{P}_0 - \mathbf{P}_1)\boldsymbol{\theta}\|^2 &= \|\mathbf{P}_D\boldsymbol{\theta}\|^2 \\ &= \|\mathbf{P}_D\mathbf{A}_r\boldsymbol{\theta}\|^2 + \|\mathbf{P}_D(\mathbf{I} - \mathbf{A}_r)\boldsymbol{\theta}\|^2 \\ &\geqslant \|\mathbf{A}_r\boldsymbol{\theta}\|^2, \end{aligned}$$

or

$$\boldsymbol{\theta}'(\mathbf{P}_0 - \mathbf{P}_1)\boldsymbol{\theta} \geqslant \boldsymbol{\theta}'\mathbf{A}_r\boldsymbol{\theta}$$

with strict equality occurring for every $\boldsymbol{\theta} \in \Omega - \omega$ if and only if $A_r \supset \omega^{\perp} \cap \Omega$.

We are now in a position to prove (6). It has been shown that (i) $r \geqslant q$, (ii) $n-p \geqslant s$, (iii) the F test is the unique consistent variance ratio test with $r = q$ and $s = n-p$, and (iv) the F test has a non-centrality parameter as large as that of any other consistent variance ratio test and that if there is a *different* test with the same non-centrality parameter then $A_r \supset \omega^{\perp} \cap \Omega$ (with strict inclusion) and $r > q$. By virtue of the remarks made near the beginning of the chapter about the power being monotonic increasing with respect to δ and s and monotonic decreasing with respect to r, it follows that $\beta(W_0, \boldsymbol{\theta}) \geqslant \beta(W, \boldsymbol{\theta})$ for every $\boldsymbol{\theta} \in \Omega - \omega$ and every $W \in C$, with equality if and only if $W = W_0$.

A brief comparison of this property with properties (2) and (3) above is given in Saw (1964).

5.2 Robustness

The distribution theory for the F test was derived on the basis of four assumptions about the errors e_i, namely (i) $E[e_i] = 0$, (ii) $\text{var}[e_i] = \sigma^2$, (iii) $\text{cov}[e_i, e_j] = 0$ for $i \neq j$, and (iv) e_i is normally distributed, each assumption holding for $i = 1, 2, \ldots, n$. The question now is: how suitable is the F statistic for testing H when there is some departure from the above assumptions? If the experiment is carefully performed so that no systematic bias is introduced (any bias can usually be removed by some process such as randomisation —cf. Cox, 1958, pp. 5, 80), then assumption (i) will be satisfied and we need only concern ourselves with the remaining three assumptions.

It transpires that the F test is remarkably robust, and as a general discussion is given in Scheffé (1959, Chapter 10) and Plackett (1960a, Chapter 4) we give only a brief summary of the effect of departures from these assumptions.

Inequality of variance has little effect on F provided the same number of observations are made on each unknown mean. For example, in testing whether two population means are equal (example, §4.2), the F test will be insensitive to differences in the two population variances, provided the number of observations on each mean is the same. If the numbers are different, inequality of variances can have considerable effect on F. Bartlett has given a modified likelihocd ratio test (Bartlett 1937, Pearson and Hartley 1954) for the equality of several variances, but the test is so sensitive to non-normality that it can be used for testing the assumption of normality. An alternative approximate test is derived by Scheffé (1959, §3.8) which makes allowances for possible non-normality. When the variances are definitely unequal, various approximate tests for H have been suggested. For example, a fundamental technique was proposed by Welch (1947, 1951) and applied by James (1951, 1954, 1956) to general univariate and multivariate linear hypotheses. Sometimes the variances can be equalised by an appropriate transformation of the data (Kempthorne, 1952, §8.5; Rao, 1952, §5e; Scheffé, 1959, §10.7; and Box and Cox, 1964).

Correlation between the errors is the most serious of the three departures and can have considerable effect on inferences based on F. Generally in scientific and industrial experiments the errors are well under control, and the experimenter can ensure that the observations are almost independent and therefore the correlations negligible. In biological and agricultural experiments this independence is usually achieved by randomisation (Cox, 1958, Chapter 5). However, in economic time-series models the observed variables occur at successive intervals of time and are usually out of the experimenter's control. In this case the errors may be serially correlated or more generally may form a stationary time-series. Testing H is then more difficult and the reader is referred to Plackett (1960a, Chapter 7) for further details.

Non-normality has little effect on the F test provided the distribution of e_i is not too skew and has well behaved "tails" (Hotelling, 1960). It is asserted that in experimental designs, normality can be approximately achieved by randomisation as the F test then approximates to the usual permutation test. Evidence supporting this assertion has been found for certain designs only and consists of (a) empirical, numerical studies, (b) theoretical, asymptotic results, and (c) moment calculations and comparisons—cf. Scheffé (1959, Chapter 9), Mitra (1960), Collier and Baker (1963), Atiqullah (1963), and Ogawa (1963).

In concluding this section we note that the above robustness properties of the F test apply also to the two-sided t test. If the one-sided t test is used it will obviously be affected considerably by skewness in the parent population.

5.3 Additional references

For a general discussion and a comprehensive list of references on the question of the behaviour of standard statistical tests under non-standard conditions, cf. Hotelling (1960). Methods for examining the departure from the standard assumptions are given in Anscombe (1960) and Box and Cox (1964).

Tests for regression coefficients when the errors are correlated: Siddiqui (1960).

Robustness of F to non-normality: Atiqullah (1962, 1964), Box and Watson (1962), Tiku (1964), Box and Tiao (1962, 1964).

CHAPTER 6

TESTING SEVERAL HYPOTHESES

6.1 The nested procedure

Let $\boldsymbol{\theta}$ be an unknown vector parameter and let G be the hypothesis that $\boldsymbol{\theta} \in \Omega$, a p-dimensional vector space. Let H_i ($i = 1, 2, \ldots, k$) be the hypothesis that $\boldsymbol{\theta} \in \omega_i$, a $p - q_i$-dimensional subspace of Ω, and denote the joint hypotheses "$\boldsymbol{\theta} \in \omega_1 \cap \omega_2$", "$\boldsymbol{\theta} \in \omega_1 \cap \omega_2 \cap \omega_3$", etc., by H_{12}, H_{123} etc. Suppose we wish to test the hypothesis $H_{12\ldots k}$ against G. Obviously we could test this hypothesis directly, but if it was rejected, we would not know why it was rejected and which H_i was responsible. What we want is a sequence of tests which tell us how much of $H_{12\ldots k}$ we can accept. One such method is the nested test procedure where we accept $H_{12\ldots k}$ against G only if all the tests H_1 against G, H_{12} against $H_1, \ldots, H_{12\ldots k}$ against $H_{12\ldots k-1}$ are not significant. The question immediately arises: is such a procedure reasonable, and what sort of power does it have as a test method? If we use the likelihood ratio as our test criterion, we have (§4.2):

$$L[H_{12\ldots k} \mid G] = L[H_1 \mid G]\, L[H_{12} \mid H_1] \ldots L[H_{12\ldots k} \mid H_{12\ldots k-1}].$$

Thus if each of the likelihood ratio statistics on the right-hand side is "near" unity then the left-hand side will also be "near" unity. This implies that if each of the nested test statistics is well below its significance level then this nested procedure is "nearly" equivalent to a direct likelihood ratio test of $H_{12\ldots k}$ against G. As the F test—and therefore the likelihood ratio test–has good power, this procedure will also have good power. Of course if the nested method led to an acceptance of $H_{12\ldots k}$ we would make a final check and carry out a direct F test of $H_{12\ldots k}$ against G.

The appropriate distribution theory for the nested method follows from the orthogonal decomposition

$$\begin{aligned} \mathbf{y} &= (\mathbf{y} - \boldsymbol{\theta}_0) + (\boldsymbol{\theta}_0 - \boldsymbol{\theta}_1) + (\boldsymbol{\theta}_1 - \boldsymbol{\theta}_{12}) + \cdots + \boldsymbol{\theta}_{12\ldots k} \\ &= (\mathbf{I} - \mathbf{P}_0)\mathbf{y} + (\mathbf{P}_0 - \mathbf{P}_1)\mathbf{y} + \cdots + \mathbf{P}_{12\ldots k}\mathbf{y} \end{aligned}$$

where $\boldsymbol{\theta}_i = \mathbf{P}_i\mathbf{y}$ and $\boldsymbol{\theta}_{12} = \mathbf{P}_{12}\mathbf{y}$, etc., are the least squares estimates of $\boldsymbol{\theta}$ for $\boldsymbol{\theta} \in \omega_i$ and $\boldsymbol{\theta} \in \omega_1 \cap \omega_2$, etc.

Since

$$\mathbf{I} = (\mathbf{I} - \mathbf{P}_0) + (\mathbf{P}_0 - \mathbf{P}_1) + \dots + \mathbf{P}_{12\dots k}$$

and the projection matrices involved are idempotent, Cochran's theorem (4.2.2) applies. Hence the quadratics

$$Q_0/\sigma^2,\ (Q_1 - Q_0)/\sigma^2,\ \dots,\ (Q_{12\dots k} - Q_{12\dots k-1})/\sigma^2$$

associated with these matrices are all distributed independently as chi-squared with $n - p$, $r_{i-1} - r_i$ $(i = 1, 2, \dots, k)$ degrees of freedom, where $r_i = \dim[\omega_1 \cap \omega_2 \cap \dots \cap \omega_i]$ and $r_0 = \dim[\Omega] = p$. The distributions are central or non-central depending on which of the H_i are true. Thus the test statistics for the nested method

$$\frac{(n-p)(Q_1-Q_0)}{(p-r_1)Q_0},\quad \frac{(n-r_1)(Q_{12}-Q_1)}{(r_1-r_2)Q_1},\quad \frac{(n-r_2)(Q_{123}-Q_{12})}{(r_2-r_3)Q_{12}},\ \text{etc.}$$

all have F distributions and the nesting procedure is continued until a significant test is obtained. We notice that the denominator or residual s.s. of each test is obtained by pooling the previous numerator and error s.s.; for this reason the nested method is essentially one of "pooling non-significant sums of squares".

The nested procedure can be applied to a set of hypotheses in which there is a natural ordering of the hypotheses. An example of this is found in polynomial regression where our basic underlying model is

$$E[y_i] = \beta_0 + \beta_1 x_i + \dots + \beta_p x_i^p \quad (i = 1, 2, \dots, n)$$

and the problem is to estimate p. The first step is to decide what is the highest value of k necessary for a polynomial approximation of the form

$$E[y_i] = \beta_0 + \beta_1 x_i + \dots + \beta_k x_i^k$$

to represent an adequate fit to the observations $\mathbf{y}$. This can be done, for example, by drawing a graph of y against x, or by taking differences if the values of x are equally spaced; sometimes the data suggest a logarithmic transformation on y_i first, followed by a regression analysis on $\log y_i$. If k is the value chosen then we apply the nested procedure to the following hypotheses $H_1 : \beta_k = 0$, $H_{12} : \beta_k = \beta_{k-1} = 0$, etc., and carry on until a significant test is obtained. Thus if the test of $\beta_j = 0$, given that $\beta_k = \beta_{k-1} = \dots = \beta_{j+1} = 0$, is the first significant test, then j is our estimate of p. Anderson (1962) has shown that apart from the desirable likelihood ratio property mentioned above, the nested method is the "best" for a certain class of reasonable test procedures.

When there is no natural ordering of a set of hypotheses the most thorough procedure would be to test all possible combinations of hypotheses using a computer. This problem arises in multiple regression where we are given the model

$$E[y_i] = \beta_0 + \beta_1 x_{i1} + \dots + \beta_p x_{ip}$$

and we wish to find out which of the β's can be put equal to zero without giving a significant increase in the residual sum of squares. Obviously the subset of β's which we leave in the regression will not be unique, especially when there are high correlations among the x's, and what we require is some criterion for choosing the best subset of β's from the class of admissible subsets. Various methods are possible on the computer, and one such technique (Garside, 1964) uses the very reasonable criterion that when comparing subsets with the same number of β's we choose the subset which gives the *smallest* non-significant increase in the residual. The reader is also referred to Ralston and Wilf (1960, Chapter 17).

However, in many situations, especially in analysis of variance applied to experimental designs, the order of nesting is immaterial because of a certain property of the system of hypotheses known as "orthogonality", and a simpler procedure, which we describe below, is available.

6.2 Orthogonality

One method for testing $H_{12\dots k}$ against G would be to accept the hypothesis if we accepted each of the k hypotheses H_i against G separately. We now ask ourselves what constraints must be put on the vector spaces Ω, ω_1, ω_2, ..., ω_k so that this separate test procedure leads to a reasonable test of $H_{12\dots k}$ against G. The separate test statistics would be

$$\frac{(n-p)}{q_i}\,\frac{\mathbf{y}'(\mathbf{P}_0 - \mathbf{P}_i)\mathbf{y}}{\mathbf{y}'(\mathbf{I} - \mathbf{P}_0)\mathbf{y}} \qquad (i = 1, 2, \dots, k)$$

and an intuitive requirement for a reasonable test would be that the test sums of squares $\mathbf{y}'(\mathbf{P}_0 - \mathbf{P}_i)\mathbf{y}$ are all statistically independent. A sufficient condition for this is $(\mathbf{P}_0 - \mathbf{P}_i)(\mathbf{P}_0 - \mathbf{P}_j) = \mathbf{0}$ for $i \neq j$ (lemma 1.9.2), and as $\mathbf{P}_0 - \mathbf{P}_i$ represents the projection on $\omega_i^p = \omega_i^\perp \cap \Omega$ (lemma 4.4.1), this condition reduces to $\omega_i^p \perp \omega_j^p$ for all i,j, $i \neq j$. We are thus led to the following definition due to Darroch and Silvey (1963). An experimental design is *orthogonal* relative to a general linear model G and linear hypotheses H_1, H_2, ..., H_k if, with this design, the subspaces Ω, ω_1, ω_2, ..., ω_k satisfy the conditions $\omega_i^p \perp \omega_j^p$ for all i,j, $i \neq j$. Since $\omega_i^p \perp \omega_j^p$ if and only if $\omega_i \oplus \Omega^\perp = (\omega_i^\perp \cap \Omega)^\perp \supset \omega_j^p$ (lemma 1.4.1), we have an equivalent definition of orthogonality, namely that $\omega_i \supset \omega_j^p$ for all i,j, $i \neq j$.

The above definition of orthogonality leads to the following theorem.

Theorem 6.2.1. The sums of squares $Q_1 - Q_0$, $Q_{12} - Q_1$, ..., $Q_{12\ldots k} - Q_{12\ldots k-1}$ are the same independent of the order of nesting the hypotheses if and only if $\omega_i^p \perp \omega_j^p$, $i \neq j$.

Proof (Sufficiency). By lemma 4.4.1, $\mathbf{P}_{12\ldots i-1} - \mathbf{P}_{12\ldots i}$ represents an orthogonal projection on

$$\begin{aligned} W_i &= \omega_1 \cap \omega_2 \cap \ldots \cap \omega_{i-1} \cap (\omega_1 \cap \omega_2 \cap \ldots \cap \omega_i)^\perp \\ &= \omega_1 \cap \ldots \cap \omega_{i-1} \cap (\omega_1^\perp + \ldots + \omega_i^\perp) \quad \text{(lemma 1.4.1)} \\ &= \omega_i^p . \end{aligned}$$

Justification for this last step is as follows: if $\boldsymbol{\theta} \in \omega_i^p$ then $\boldsymbol{\theta} \in \omega_i^\perp$, $\boldsymbol{\theta} \in \omega_1 \cap \ldots \cap \omega_{i-1}$ (by the alternative definition of orthogonality) and $\boldsymbol{\theta} \in W_i$. Alternatively if $\boldsymbol{\theta} \in W_i$ then for some $\boldsymbol{\alpha}_1, \ldots, \boldsymbol{\alpha}_i$,

$$\boldsymbol{\theta} = \mathbf{P}_{12\ldots i-1}\boldsymbol{\theta} = \mathbf{P}_{12\ldots i-1} \sum_{j=1}^{i} (\mathbf{I} - \mathbf{P}_j)\boldsymbol{\alpha}_j ,$$

leading to

$$\boldsymbol{\theta} = \mathbf{P}_{12\ldots i-1}(\mathbf{I} - \mathbf{P}_i)\boldsymbol{\alpha}_i = \mathbf{P}_{12\ldots i-1}(\mathbf{P}_0 - \mathbf{P}_i)\boldsymbol{\alpha}_i = (\mathbf{P}_0 - \mathbf{P}_i)\boldsymbol{\alpha}_i$$

and $\boldsymbol{\theta} \in \omega_i^p$. Thus

$$\mathbf{P}_{12\ldots i-1} - \mathbf{P}_{12\ldots i} = \mathbf{P}_0 - \mathbf{P}_i$$

and the sums of squares are equal to $Q_i - Q_0$ for $i = 1, 2, \ldots, k$ which are independent of the order of nesting. This completes the proof that the conditions are sufficient.

EXERCISE 10. Prove that the conditions $\omega_i^p \perp \omega_j^p$ are also necessary.

Having established the definition of orthogonality we can now demonstrate, using the above theorem, that the separate test method for testing $H_{12\ldots k}$ against G is a reasonable one when we have orthogonality. The following justification of the separate method is due to Darroch and Silvey (1963).

$$\left\{L\left[H_{12\ldots k} \mid G\right]\right\}^{-2/n} - 1 = \frac{(Q_{12\ldots k} - Q_0)}{Q_0}, \quad \text{(cf. §4.1)}$$

$$= \frac{(Q_1 - Q_0) + (Q_{12} - Q_1) + \dots + (Q_{12\dots k} - Q_{12\dots k-1})}{Q_0}$$

$$= \sum_{i=1}^{k} \frac{(Q_i - Q_0)}{Q_0}$$

$$= \sum_{i=1}^{k} \left(\left\{ L\left[H_i \mid G\right] \right\}^{-2/n} - 1 \right).$$

If each $L[H_i \mid G]$ is "near" unity then $L[H_{12\dots k} \mid G]$ is "near" unity, and by the same argument applied to the nested test procedure we see that the separate test method will also have good power.

The idea of orthogonality is usually associated with those experimental designs in which the least squares estimates of certain parameters are uncorrelated. Suppose Ω takes the range space form $\boldsymbol{\theta} = \mathbf{X}\boldsymbol{\beta}$, where $\mathbf{X}$ is an $n \times r$ matrix of rank p $(p < r)$ and $\mathbf{H}\boldsymbol{\beta} = \mathbf{0}$ are suitable identifiability conditions. Let $\mathbf{X}$ be partitioned into $k+1$ submatrices $(\mathbf{X}_c, \mathbf{X}_1, \mathbf{X}_2, \dots, \mathbf{X}_k)$ with a corresponding partition of $\boldsymbol{\beta}' = (\boldsymbol{\beta}'_c, \boldsymbol{\beta}'_1, \dots, \boldsymbol{\beta}'_k)$ and $\mathbf{H}$. We are interested in testing the hypotheses $H_i : \boldsymbol{\beta}_i = \mathbf{0}$ $(i = 1, 2, \dots, k)$. Then $\omega_i = \{\boldsymbol{\theta} : \boldsymbol{\theta} = \mathbf{X}_i^* \boldsymbol{\beta}_i^*,\ \mathbf{H}_i^* \boldsymbol{\beta}_i^* = \mathbf{0}\}$, where $\mathbf{X}_i^*$ is the matrix $\mathbf{X}$ with the submatrix $\mathbf{X}_i$ deleted; $\mathbf{H}_i^*$ and $\boldsymbol{\beta}_i^*$ are similarly defined. We shall now prove that the least squares estimates $\boldsymbol{\beta}_{i0}$ of $\boldsymbol{\beta}_i$ $(i = 1, 2, \dots, k)$ for $\boldsymbol{\theta} \in \Omega$ are uncorrelated if and only if we have orthogonality. The proof rests on the following lemma.

Lemma 6.2.2. Let Ω be a vector space and let $\mathbf{A}_i$ be any matrix such that $\omega_i = N[\mathbf{A}_i] \cap \Omega$ is a subspace of Ω. Then $\omega_i^p \perp \omega_j^p$ if and only if $\mathbf{A}_i \mathbf{P}_0 \mathbf{A}'_j = \mathbf{0}$.

Proof. We note first of all that $\mathbf{A}_i\boldsymbol{\theta} = \mathbf{0}$ implies that $\mathbf{A}_i \mathbf{P}_0 \boldsymbol{\theta} = \mathbf{0}$ when $\boldsymbol{\theta} \in \Omega$ and we can therefore assume that $\mathbf{A}_i \mathbf{P}_0 \neq \mathbf{0}$ since $\omega_i \neq \Omega$.

From lemma 4.4.2 we have that

$$\omega_i^{\perp} \cap \Omega = R[\mathbf{P}_0 \mathbf{A}'_i]$$

and therefore $\omega_i^p \perp \omega_j^p$ if and only if $\mathbf{A}_i \mathbf{P}_0 \mathbf{A}'_j = \mathbf{0}$.

Corollary 6.2.3. If $\Omega = N[\mathbf{A}]$ and $\mathbf{A}\mathbf{A}'_i = \mathbf{0}$ for $i = 1, 2, \dots, k$ then $\omega_i^p \perp \omega_j^p$ if and only if $\mathbf{A}_i \mathbf{A}'_j = \mathbf{0}$. The proof of this follows from example 3, §3.4; thus

$$\begin{aligned} \mathbf{A}_i \mathbf{P}_0 \mathbf{A}'_j &= \mathbf{A}_i (\mathbf{I} - \bar{\mathbf{A}}'(\bar{\mathbf{A}}\bar{\mathbf{A}}')^{-1}\bar{\mathbf{A}})\mathbf{A}'_j \\ &= \mathbf{A}_i \mathbf{A}'_j, \end{aligned}$$

where $\bar{\mathbf{A}}$ is the matrix of linearly independent rows of $\mathbf{A}$.

We are now in a position to prove the following theorem:

Theorem 6.2.4. The vectors $\boldsymbol{\beta}_{i0}$ and $\boldsymbol{\beta}_{j0}$ are uncorrelated if and only if $\omega_i^p \perp \omega_j^p$.

Proof. Since the constraints $\mathbf{H}\boldsymbol{\beta} = \mathbf{0}$ are suitable for identifiability we have from theorem 3.4.1,

$$\mathbf{P}_0 = \mathbf{X}(\mathbf{G}'\mathbf{G})^{-1}\mathbf{X}' \quad \text{and} \quad \mathbf{H}(\mathbf{G}'\mathbf{G})^{-1}\mathbf{X}' = \mathbf{0}. \qquad (6.2.1)$$

Now $\boldsymbol{\beta} = (\mathbf{G}'\mathbf{G})^{-1}\mathbf{X}'\boldsymbol{\theta}$, and the hypothesis that $\boldsymbol{\beta}_i = \mathbf{0}$ is equivalent to $\mathbf{B}_i\boldsymbol{\beta} = \mathbf{0}$, where $\mathbf{B}_i$, if partitioned in the same way as $\mathbf{X}$, has the identity matrix in the $(i+1)$th partition and zero matrices elsewhere. Thus, testing the hypothesis H_i is equivalent to testing $\mathbf{B}_i(\mathbf{G}'\mathbf{G})^{-1}\mathbf{X}'\boldsymbol{\theta} = \mathbf{A}_i\boldsymbol{\theta} = \mathbf{0}$, and from lemma 6.2.2, $\omega_i^p \perp \omega_j^p$ if and only if

$$\mathbf{B}_i(\mathbf{G}'\mathbf{G})^{-1}\mathbf{X}'\mathbf{X}(\mathbf{G}'\mathbf{G})^{-1}\mathbf{X}'\mathbf{X}(\mathbf{G}'\mathbf{G})^{-1}\mathbf{B}_j' = \mathbf{0}$$

or, using equation (6.2.1)

$$\mathbf{B}_i(\mathbf{G}'\mathbf{G})^{-1}\mathbf{X}'\mathbf{X}(\mathbf{G}'\mathbf{G})^{-1}\mathbf{B}_j' = \mathbf{0}.$$

But

$$\begin{aligned} \operatorname{cov}(\boldsymbol{\beta}_{i0}, \boldsymbol{\beta}_{j0}) &= E[(\boldsymbol{\beta}_{i0} - \boldsymbol{\beta}_i)(\boldsymbol{\beta}_{j0} - \boldsymbol{\beta}_j)] \\ &= \mathbf{B}_i D[\boldsymbol{\beta}_0]\mathbf{B}_j' \\ &= \sigma^2 \mathbf{B}_i(\mathbf{G}'\mathbf{G})^{-1}\mathbf{X}'\mathbf{X}(\mathbf{G}'\mathbf{G})^{-1}\mathbf{B}_j' \end{aligned}$$

and therefore we have orthogonality if and only if $\operatorname{cov}(\boldsymbol{\beta}_{i0}, \boldsymbol{\beta}_{j0}) = \mathbf{0}$.

6.3 Orthogonality in complete two-way layouts

Consider a two-factor analysis of variance with factors A and B at I and J levels respectively, and suppose that n_{ij} observations $y_{ij1}, y_{ij2}, \ldots$ etc. are made on the combination ϕ_{ij} of the ith level of A with the jth level of B. This gives us the model $y_{ijk} = \theta_{ijk} + e_{ijk}$ for $k = 1, 2, \ldots, n_{ij}$, $i = 1, 2, \ldots, I$; $j = 1, 2, \ldots, J$, where $\theta_{ijk} = \phi_{ij}$; the random errors e_{ijk} are all independently $\mathcal{N}[0, \sigma^2]$. We now split up the i,jth cell mean ϕ_{ij} into an overall mean μ, an effect α_i due to the ith level of A, an effect β_j due to the jth level of B, and an interaction term γ_{ij}; thus $\phi_{ij} = \mu + \alpha_i + \beta_j + \gamma_{ij}$. If we write the elements $\{y_{ijk}\}$, $\{\theta_{ijk}\}$ and $\{e_{ijk}\}$ as single $n_{..}$-dimensional vectors (where $n_{..} = \sum_i\sum_j n_{ij}$) we can express the above model in the range space form $\mathbf{y} = \boldsymbol{\theta} + \mathbf{e}$ with $G: \boldsymbol{\theta} = \mathbf{X}\boldsymbol{\delta}$, where $\boldsymbol{\delta}' = (\mu, \alpha_1, \ldots, \alpha_I, \beta_1, \ldots, \beta_J, \gamma_{11}, \gamma_{12}, \cdots \gamma_{IJ})$. Since we have replaced the IJ uniquely defined parameters ϕ_{ij} by $IJ + I + J + 1$ new parameters, $\boldsymbol{\delta}$ will not be identifiable and we must introduce identifiability constraints. The form of these constraints will depend on what "weights" we choose for defining these parameters. For example, the observations for certain i, j cells may be more important than the others, and therefore we would wish to give more weight to these observations. Thus we may define our parameters as follows:

The means for the ith level of A and the jth level of B are defined to be $a_i = \sum_j v_j \phi_{ij}$ and $b_j = \sum_i u_i \phi_{ij}$ where all the $u_i \geqslant 0$, $v_j \geqslant 0$ and $\sum_i u_i = \sum_j v_j = 1$. The general mean μ is defined to be

$$\mu = \sum_i u_i a_i = \sum_j v_j b_j = \sum_i \sum_j u_i v_j \phi_{ij} .$$

The main effect of the ith level of A is defined by

$$\alpha_i = a_i - \mu$$

and the main effect of the jth level of B is defined by

$$\beta_j = b_j - \mu .$$

Now $\phi_{ij} = \mu + \alpha_i + \beta_j + \gamma_{ij}$, where

$$\gamma_{ij} = \phi_{ij} - \sum_j v_j \phi_{ij} - \sum_i u_i \phi_{ij} + \sum_i \sum_j u_i v_j \phi_{ij} ,$$

is called the interaction between the ith level of A and the jth level of B. By defining the main effects and interactions as above we have effectively imposed the identifiability constraints

$$\sum_i u_i \alpha_i = \sum_j v_j \beta_j = \sum_i u_i \gamma_{ij} = \sum_j v_j \gamma_{ij} = 0 .$$

Finally let $\nu_{ijk} = \theta_{ijk} - \bar{\theta}_{ij.}$, where $\bar{\theta}_{ij.} = \sum_k \theta_{ijk}/n_{ij}$, then our model now takes the form

$$\theta_{ijk} = \mu + \alpha_i + \beta_j + \gamma_{ij} + \nu_{ijk} ,$$

where the α_i, β_j, γ_{ij} are defined as above with $\bar{\theta}_{ij.}$ replacing ϕ_{ij} in the definitions. We now consider testing the following hypotheses H_1, H_2 and H_3 against G, where

$$G : \nu_{ijk} = 0,$$

$$H_1 : \nu_{ijk} = 0, \quad \gamma_{ij} = 0 \qquad \text{(interactions zero)}$$

$$H_2 : \nu_{ijk} = 0, \quad \alpha_i = 0 \qquad \text{(main effects of } A \text{ zero)}$$

$$H_3 : \nu_{ijk} = 0, \quad \beta_j = 0 \qquad \text{(main effects of } B \text{ zero)}$$

$$H_4 : \nu_{ijk} = 0, \quad \mu = 0,$$

and in the following theorem we derive necessary and sufficient conditions for this system of hypotheses to be orthogonal.

Theorem 6.3.1. The hypotheses $H_1, \ldots, H_4$ are orthogonal with respect to G if and only if

$$n_{ij} = n_{i.}\, n_{.j}/n_{..}, \quad u_i = n_{i.}/n_{..} \quad \text{and}$$
$$v_j = n_{.j}/n_{..} \quad \text{for all } i, j.$$

Proof. Let $\boldsymbol{\theta}$ be the $n_{..}$-dimensional column vector with elements θ_{ijk}; we can express the hypotheses in the form

$$G : \mathbf{A}\boldsymbol{\theta} = \mathbf{0} \quad \text{and} \quad H_p : \mathbf{A}\boldsymbol{\theta} = \mathbf{0},\ \mathbf{A}_p\boldsymbol{\theta} = \mathbf{0}$$

for $p = 1, 2, 3, 4$. For example, we wish to express the conditions

$$\nu_{ijk} = \theta_{ijk} - \sum_k \theta_{ijk}/n_{ij} = 0 \qquad (6.3.1)$$

in the form $\mathbf{A}\boldsymbol{\theta} = 0$. The matrix $\mathbf{A}$ would be $n_{..} \times n_{..}$ and the row corresponding to equation (6.3.1) would have the (r_0, s_0, t_0) element of the form

$$\delta_{ir_0}\delta_{js_0}\delta_{kt_0} - \delta_{ir_0}\delta_{js_0}/n_{r_0 s_0} \qquad (6.3.2)$$

where δ_{ab} is the Kronecker delta. Now

$$\gamma_{ij} = \bar{\theta}_{ij.} - \sum_j v_j\,\bar{\theta}_{ij.} - \sum_i u_i\,\bar{\theta}_{ij.} + \sum_i\sum_j u_i\,v_j\,\bar{\theta}_{ij.}$$

and the row of $\mathbf{A}_1$ corresponding to $\gamma_{i_1 j_1} = 0$ has its (r_1, s_1, t_1) element as

$$(\delta_{i_1 r_1}\delta_{j_1 s_1} - v_{s_1}\delta_{i_1 r_1} - u_{r_1}\delta_{j_1 s_1} + u_{r_1}v_{s_1})/n_{r_1 s_1}. \qquad (6.3.3)$$

Similarly the (r_2, s_2, t_2) element of row $\alpha_{i_2} = 0$ for the matrix $\mathbf{A}_2$ is

$$(\delta_{i_2 r_2}v_{s_2} - u_{r_2}v_{s_2})/n_{r_2 s_2}, \qquad (6.3.4)$$

the (r_3, s_3, t_3) element of row $\beta_{j_3} = 0$ for $\mathbf{A}_3$ is

$$(\delta_{j_3 s_3}u_{r_3} - u_{r_3}v_{s_3})/n_{r_3 s_3} \qquad (6.3.5)$$

and the (r_4, s_4, t_4) element of $\mu = 0$ is

$$u_{r_4}v_{s_4}/n_{r_4 s_4}. \qquad (6.3.6)$$

By multiplying together (6.3.2) and (6.3.3), putting $r_0 = r_1$, $s_0 = s_1$, $t_0 = t_1$ and summing on r_0, s_0, t_0 ($t_0 = 1, 2, \ldots, n_{r_0 s_0}$; $r_0 = 1, 2, \ldots, I$; $s_0 = 1, 2, \ldots, J$) we have $\mathbf{A}_1\mathbf{A}' = \mathbf{0}$. Similarly $\mathbf{A}_2\mathbf{A}' = \mathbf{A}_3\mathbf{A}' = \mathbf{A}_4\mathbf{A}' = \mathbf{0}$ since (6.3.2) is the only term above containing t_0, and this summed on t_0 is zero. Thus by corollary 6.2.3, the hypotheses are orthogonal if and only if $\mathbf{A}_p\mathbf{A}_q' = \mathbf{0}$ for all p, q, $p \neq q$, and we now show that these matrix conditions hold if and only if

$$n_{ij} = n_{i.}n_{.j}/n_{..}, \quad u_i = n_{i.}/n_{..} \quad \text{and} \quad v_j = n_{.j}/n_{..} \quad \text{for all } i, j.$$

(a) *Sufficiency*. If these conditions on the n_{ij}, u_i, v_j hold, then (6.3.3) becomes

$$n_{..}(\delta_{i_1 r_1}/n_{r_1.} - 1/n_{..})(\delta_{j_1 s_1}/n_{.s_1} - 1/n_{..}). \tag{6.3.7}$$

Therefore by multiplying (6.3.4) and (6.3.7) together, putting $r_1 = r_2$, $s_1 = s_2$ and summing on r_1, s_1, t_1 we have $\mathbf{A}_1\mathbf{A}_2' = \mathbf{0}$. In a similar manner it can be shown that $\mathbf{A}_1\mathbf{A}_3' = \ldots = \mathbf{A}_3\mathbf{A}_4' = \mathbf{0}$. Hence the hypotheses are orthogonal and the conditions are sufficient.

(b) *Necessity*. Given that $\mathbf{A}_1\mathbf{A}_4' = \mathbf{0}$, we multiply (6.3.3) and (6.3.6) together, set $r_1 = r_4$, $s_1 = s_4$, and sum on r_1, s_1, t_1. This gives us an element of $\mathbf{A}_1\mathbf{A}_4'$, and therefore

$$\frac{u_{i_1} v_{j_1}}{n_{i_1 j_1}} - \sum_{s_1}\left\{\frac{u_{i_1} v_{s_1}^2}{n_{i_1 s_1}}\right\} - \sum_{r_1}\left\{\frac{v_{j_1} u_{r_1}^2}{n_{r_1 j_1}}\right\} + \sum_{r_1}\sum_{s_1}\left\{\frac{u_{r_1}^2 v_{s_1}^2}{n_{r_1 s_1}}\right\} = 0 \tag{6.3.8}$$

Similarly from $\mathbf{A}_2\mathbf{A}_4' = \mathbf{A}_3\mathbf{A}_4' = \mathbf{0}$ we obtain

$$u_{i_2}\sum_{s_2}\left\{\frac{v_{s_2}^2}{n_{i_2 s_2}}\right\} - \sum_{r_2}\sum_{s_2}\left\{\frac{u_{r_2}^2 v_{s_2}^2}{n_{r_2 s_2}}\right\} = 0 \tag{6.3.9}$$

and

$$v_{j_3}\sum_{r_3}\left\{\frac{u_{r_3}^2}{n_{r_3 j_3}}\right\} - \sum_{r_3}\sum_{s_3}\left\{\frac{u_{r_3}^2 v_{s_3}^2}{n_{r_3 s_3}}\right\} = 0 \tag{6.3.10}$$

From these last two equations we note that $u_{i_2} > 0$ and $v_{j_3} > 0$ for all i_2 and j_3. Adding (6.3.10) to (6.3.8), putting $j_1 = j_3$, and dividing by u_{i_1}, we obtain

$$\frac{v_{j_1}}{n_{i_1 j_1}} - \sum_{s_1}\left\{\frac{v_{s_1}^2}{n_{i_1 s_1}}\right\} = 0. \tag{6.3.11}$$

Multiplying this equation by $n_{i_1 j_1}$ and summing on j_1 gives

$$1 - n_{i_1.}\sum_{s_1}\{v_{s_1}^2/n_{i_1 s_1}\} = 0.$$

Substituting this back in (6.3.11) leads to

$$v_{j_1} = n_{i_1 j_1}/n_{i_1.} = n_{.j_1}/n_{..}.$$

In a similar manner it is readily shown that

$$u_{i_1} = n_{i_1 j_1}/n_{.j_1} = n_{i_1.}/n_{..}\,.$$

Now by multiplying (6.3.4) and (6.3.5) together, putting $r_2 = r_3$, $s_2 = s_3$ and summing on r_2, s_2, t_2 gives us an element of $\mathbf{A}_2\mathbf{A}_3'$. Thus if $\mathbf{A}_2\mathbf{A}_3' = \mathbf{0}$ we have, using the above values for the weights u_i and v_j,

$$0 = \sum_{r_2}\sum_{s_2}\sum_{t_2}\left\{\left(\frac{\delta_{i_2 r_2}}{n_{r_2.}} - \frac{1}{n_{..}}\right)\left(\frac{\delta_{j_3 s_2}}{n_{.s_2}} - \frac{1}{n_{..}}\right)\right\}$$

$$= n_{i_2 j_3}/n_{i_2.}n_{.j_3} - 1/n_{..}$$

for every i_2 and j_3. Therefore a necessary condition for orthogonality is that $n_{ij} = n_{i.}n_{.j}/n_{..}$ for all i, j and this completes the proof of the theorem.

We note that when we have an equal number of observations per cell the conditions for orthogonality are automatically satisfied, provided we use equal weights. In this case the identifiability constraints reduce to $\sum_i \alpha_i = \sum_j \beta_j = \sum_i \gamma_{ij} = \sum_j \gamma_{ij} = 0$.

When the hypotheses are orthogonal, we have from theorem 6.2.4 that the least squares estimates of μ, $\{\alpha_i\}$, $\{\beta_j\}$ and $\{\gamma_{ij}\}$ for $\boldsymbol{\theta} \in \Omega$ are uncorrelated groupwise and are very easily derived, as we shall see below, by using the Gauss–Markov theorem. In what follows we shall assume that $u_i = n_{i.}/n_{..}$,

$$v_j = n_{.j}/n_{..}, \quad \text{and} \quad n_{ij} = n_{i.}n_{.j}/n_{..} \quad \text{for all } i, j.$$

To find the least squares estimates of μ, α_i, etc. for G, we require the least squares estimates of $\mathbf{A}_p\boldsymbol{\theta}$ ($p = 1, 2, 3, 4$, $\boldsymbol{\theta} \in \Omega$). From the Gauss–Markov theorem 3.5.1 these are given by $\mathbf{A}_p\mathbf{P}_0\mathbf{y}$ which is just $\mathbf{A}_p\mathbf{y}$ since $\mathbf{A}_p\mathbf{A}' = \mathbf{0}$ (cf. corollary 6.2.3). Therefore the least squares estimates μ_0, α_{i0}, etc. can be written down immediately from the definitions of the parameters, namely

$$\mu_0 = \sum_i\sum_j n_{i.}n_{.j}\bar{y}_{ij.}/n_{..}^2$$

$$= \sum_i\sum_j\sum_k y_{ijk}/n_{..}$$

$$= \bar{y}_{...} \quad \text{say,}$$

$$\gamma_{ij0} = \bar{y}_{ij.} - \sum_j n_{.j}\bar{y}_{ij.}/n_{..} - \sum_i n_{i.}\bar{y}_{ij.}/n_{..} + \bar{y}_{...}$$

$$\alpha_{i0} = \sum_j n_{.j}\bar{y}_{ij.}/n_{..} - \bar{y}_{...}$$

and

$$\beta_{j0} = \sum_i n_{i.}\bar{y}_{ij.}/n_{..} - \bar{y}_{...}\,.$$

Suppose we wish to test $H_1 : \nu_{ijk} = 0,\ \gamma_{ij} = 0$ or $\boldsymbol{\theta} \in \omega_1$, say, then we require the least squares estimates of $\mathbf{A}_p\boldsymbol{\theta}$ ($p = 2, 3, 4$) for $\boldsymbol{\theta} \in \omega_1$; namely $\mathbf{A}_p\mathbf{P}_1\,\mathbf{y}$. Now $\mathbf{I} - \mathbf{P}_1$ represents the projection on $R[(\mathbf{A}', \mathbf{A}_1')]$ (by lemma 1.2.1) which is orthogonal to $R[\mathbf{A}_p']$ for $p = 2, 3, 4$. Hence $(\mathbf{I} - \mathbf{P}_1)\mathbf{A}_p' = \mathbf{0}$

and
$$\mathbf{A}_p\boldsymbol{\theta}_1 = \mathbf{A}_p\mathbf{y} = \mathbf{A}_p\boldsymbol{\theta}_0 \quad \text{for} \quad p = 2, 3, 4.$$

This means that the least squares estimates of μ, α_i and β_j remain unchanged when $\gamma_{ij} = 0$ and do not have to be recalculated. The reason for this is that the orthogonality of $G, H_1, \ldots, H_4$ implies that the groups of estimates are uncorrelated, and therefore independent, under the assumption of normality. Thus the least squares estimates of any one group, say the $\{\alpha_i\}$, are independent of the values of the parameters in the other groups μ, $\{\gamma_{ij}\}$, $\{\beta_j\}$.

The numerator s.s., $\|\boldsymbol{\theta}_0 - \boldsymbol{\theta}_1\|^2$, for the F test of H_1 is simply $\sum_i\sum_j n_{ij}\gamma_{ij0}^2$ since the i, j, kth element of $\boldsymbol{\theta}_0 - \boldsymbol{\theta}_1$ is $(\mu_0 + \alpha_{i0} + \beta_{j0} + \gamma_{ij0}) - (\mu_0 + \alpha_{i0} + \beta_{j0})$ or γ_{ij0}. Similarly we have

$$\|\boldsymbol{\theta}_1 - \boldsymbol{\theta}_{12}\|^2 = \|\boldsymbol{\theta}_0 - \boldsymbol{\theta}_2\|^2 = \sum_i n_{i.}\,\alpha_{i0}^2$$
$$\|\boldsymbol{\theta}_{12} - \boldsymbol{\theta}_{123}\|^2 = \|\boldsymbol{\theta}_0 - \boldsymbol{\theta}_3\|^2 = \sum_j n_{.j}\beta_{j0}^2$$
$$\|\boldsymbol{\theta}_{123} - \boldsymbol{\theta}_{1234}\|^2 = \|\boldsymbol{\theta}_0 - \boldsymbol{\theta}_4\|^2 = n_{..}\,\mu_0^2$$

and
$$\theta_{ijk0} = \mu_0 + \alpha_{i0} + \beta_{j0} + \gamma_{ij0} = \bar{y}_{ij.}\,.$$

We note that $\boldsymbol{\theta}_{1234} = \mathbf{0}$ and therefore $\|\boldsymbol{\theta}_{123}\|^2 = n_{..}\,\mu_0^2$. Thus corresponding to the decomposition
$$\theta_{ijk} = \mu + \alpha_i + \beta_j + \gamma_{ij} + \nu_{ijk}$$
we have a similar decomposition
$$y_{ijk} = \bar{y}_{...} + \alpha_{i0} + \beta_{j0} + \gamma_{ij0} + y_{ijk} - \bar{y}_{ij}.$$
Squaring both sides and summing on i, j, k we find that the cross-product terms vanish because of orthogonality, giving
$$\sum_i\sum_j\sum_k y_{ijk}^2 = n\mu_0^2 + \sum_i n_{i.}\,\alpha_{i0}^2 + \sum_j n_{.j}\beta_{j0}^2 + \sum_i\sum_j n_{ij}\gamma_{ij0}^2 + \sum_i\sum_j\sum_k (y_{ijk} - \bar{y}_{ij.})^2.$$
We recall that this corresponds to the decomposition
$$\mathbf{I} = \mathbf{P}_{123} + (\mathbf{P}_1 - \mathbf{P}_{12}) + (\mathbf{P}_{12} - \mathbf{P}_{123}) + (\mathbf{P}_0 - \mathbf{P}_1) + (\mathbf{I} - \mathbf{P}_0).$$

In general we usually consider the total variation about the mean, namely

$$\mathbf{y}'(\mathbf{I}-\mathbf{P}_{123})\mathbf{y} = \sum_i \sum_j \sum_k y_{ijk}^2 - n_{..}\mu_0^2$$
$$= \sum_i \sum_j \sum_k (y_{ijk} - \bar{y}_{...})^2$$

and construct the following analysis of variance table.

Source	s.s.	d.f.	m.s.s.
Between rows	$\sum_i n_{i.}\alpha_{i0}^2$	$I-1$	m.s.s. (2)
Between columns	$\sum_j n_{.j}\beta_{j0}^2$	$J-1$	m.s.s. (3)
Interactions	$\sum_i \sum_j n_{ij}\gamma_{ij0}^2$	$(I-1)(J-1)$	m.s.s. (1)
Residual	$\sum_i \sum_j \sum_k (y_{ijk} - \bar{y}_{ij.})^2$	$n_{..} - IJ$	m.s.s. (r)
Corrected total	$\sum_i \sum_j \sum_k (y_{ijk} - \bar{y}_{...})^2$	$n_{..} - 1$	
Correction for mean	$n_{..}\bar{y}_{...}^2$	1	
Total	$\sum_i \sum_j \sum_k y_{ijk}^2$	$n_{..}$	

Here the terms "row" and "column" refer to the levels of factors A and B respectively. The test statistic for testing H_p is simply

$$F = \frac{\text{m.s.s. }(p)}{\text{m.s.s. }(r)} \qquad p = 1, 2, 3,$$

where m.s.s. as usual denotes the appropriate s.s. divided by its degrees of freedom. In general we are not interested in testing $H_4 : \mu = 0$, but if we accept hypothesis H_{123} we may be interested in finding confidence intervals for μ. These can be calculated from $n^{1/2}(\bar{y}_{...} - \mu)/(\text{m.s.s. }(r))$ which has the t distribution with $n_{..} - IJ$ degrees of freedom.

The column giving the degrees of freedom for each s.s. is obtained by calculating the number of independent contrasts in $\mathbf{A}_p\boldsymbol{\theta}$ for $p = 1$, 2, 3. Thus $\boldsymbol{\alpha} = \mathbf{A}_2\boldsymbol{\theta}$ has $(I-1)$ independent constraints as there exists one identifiability condition $\sum_i n_{i.}\alpha_i = 0$. Similarly $\sum_i n_{i.}\gamma_{ij} = \sum_j n_{.j}\gamma_{ij} = 0$, and $\boldsymbol{\gamma} = \mathbf{A}_1\boldsymbol{\theta}$ has $IJ - I - J + 1$ or $(I-1)(J-1)$ independent constraints.

6.4 Complete higher-way layouts

The ideas developed in the previous section can be extended to complete layouts with more than two factors. For example, consider the three-way layout $y_{ijkl} = \theta_{ijkl} + e_{ijkl}$ for $i = 1, 2, \dots, I$; $j = 1, 2, \dots, J$; $k = 1, 2, \dots, K$; $l = 1, 2, \dots, L$, and

$$\theta_{ijkl} = \phi_{ijk} = \bar{\theta}_{ijk.} \, .$$

Here we assume that there are an equal number L of observations in each cell, and using equal weights we define the following interactions and main effects:

$$\begin{aligned}
\nu_{ijkl} &= \theta_{ijkl} - \bar{\theta}_{ijk.} \\
\pi_{ijk} &= \bar{\theta}_{ijk.} - \bar{\theta}_{ij..} - \bar{\theta}_{i.k.} - \bar{\theta}_{.jk.} + \bar{\theta}_{i...} + \bar{\theta}_{.j..} + \bar{\theta}_{..k.} - \bar{\theta}_{....} \\
\gamma_{jk}^{(23)} &= \bar{\theta}_{.jk.} - \bar{\theta}_{.j..} - \bar{\theta}_{..k.} + \bar{\theta}_{....} \\
\gamma_{ik}^{(13)} &= \bar{\theta}_{i.k.} - \bar{\theta}_{i...} - \bar{\theta}_{..k.} + \bar{\theta}_{....} \\
\gamma_{ij}^{(12)} &= \bar{\theta}_{ij..} - \bar{\theta}_{i...} - \bar{\theta}_{.j..} + \bar{\theta}_{....} \\
\alpha_i^{(1)} &= \bar{\theta}_{i...} - \bar{\theta}_{....} \\
\alpha_j^{(2)} &= \bar{\theta}_{.j..} - \bar{\theta}_{....} \\
\alpha_k^{(3)} &= \bar{\theta}_{..k.} - \bar{\theta}_{....} \\
\mu &= \bar{\theta}_{....}
\end{aligned}$$

where $\bar{\theta}_{ij..} = \sum_k \sum_l \theta_{ijkl}/KL$ etc. Then

$$\theta_{ijkl} = \nu_{ijkl} + \mu + \alpha_i^{(1)} + \alpha_j^{(2)} + \alpha_k^{(3)} + \gamma_{jk}^{(23)} + \gamma_{ik}^{(13)} + \gamma_{ij}^{(12)} + \pi_{ijk} \, ,$$

and we assume $G : \nu_{ijkl} = 0$. The hypotheses of interest are the hypotheses that the groups of parameters μ, $\{\alpha_i^{(1)}\}$, $\{\gamma_{jk}^{(23)}\}$, $\{\pi_{ijk}\}$, etc. are zero, given that the $\{\nu_{ijkl}\}$ are zero.

Changing the notation slightly from that of §6.3, we denote the matrices corresponding to the null space representations of these hypotheses by $\mathbf{1}_n'$ (where $n = IJKL$), $\mathbf{A}_p$, $\mathbf{A}_{pq}$, $\mathbf{A}_{123}$ respectively; also $\mathbf{A}$ denotes the matrix corresponding to G. Now it is readily seen that, apart from μ, all the other parameters are contrasts in θ_{ijkl} and therefore $\mathbf{A}\mathbf{1}_n = \mathbf{A}_p\mathbf{1}_n = \mathbf{A}_{pq}\mathbf{1}_n = \mathbf{A}_{123}\mathbf{1}_n = \mathbf{0}$. Also the contrasts are orthogonal groupwise, that is the various matrix products $\mathbf{A}\mathbf{A}_p'$, $\mathbf{A}\mathbf{A}_{pq}'$, $\mathbf{A}_p\mathbf{A}_{pq}'$, $\mathbf{A}_p\mathbf{A}_q'$, etc., are all zero. It therefore follows from corollary

6.2.3 that we have orthogonality, and the least squares estimates of the parameters remain the same for testing the above hypotheses.

This method of proof can obviously be extended to deal with complete higher-way layouts with equal numbers of observations per cell. For further details concerning complete layouts the reader is referred to Scheffé, Chapter 4.

6.5 Orthogonality in experimental designs

Consider a randomised block design with I treatments and J blocks. Let y_{ij} be the observation for the ith treatment on the jth block, and assume the model $E[y_{ij}] = \theta_{ij} = \mu + \alpha_i + \beta_j$ for $i = 1, 2, \ldots, I$ and $j = 1, 2, \ldots, J$. This is the same model as for the two-way layout of §6.3, except that the treatment × block interactions are assumed to be negligible and there is only one observation per cell. As before, we use weights $\{u_i\}$ and $\{v_j\}$, giving the identifiability constraints $\sum_i u_i \alpha_i = \sum_j v_j \beta_j = 0$. We now consider the hypotheses

$$H_1 : \theta_{ij} = \mu + \beta_j\,, \quad H_2 : \theta_{ij} = \mu + \alpha_i, \quad H_3 : \theta_{ij} = \alpha_i + \beta_j$$

and find what form the weights must take for H_1, H_2 and H_3 to be orthogonal with respect to G, the hypothesis of zero interactions.

Theorem 6.5.1. The hypotheses H_1, H_2 and H_3 are orthogonal with respect to G if and only if $u_i = 1/I$ and $v_j = 1/J$.

Proof

(a) *Necessity.* From the alternative form of the definition of orthogonality (§6.2) we have that the hypotheses are orthogonal if and only if $\omega_i^\perp \cap \Omega \subset \omega_j$ for $i \neq j$. Thus a necessary condition for orthogonality is that $\omega_3^\perp \cap \Omega \subset \omega_1 \cap \omega_2$. The vector space $\omega_3^\perp \cap \Omega$ is defined by the set of $\theta_{ij} = \mu + \alpha_i + \beta_j$ such that

$$\sum_i \sum_j (\alpha_i^* + \beta_j^*)(\mu + \alpha_i + \beta_j) = 0 \qquad (6.5.1)$$

for every α_i^* and β_j^*. If this set of θ_{ij} also belongs to $\omega_1 \cap \omega_2$ then θ_{ij} must be constant with respect to i and j and $\alpha_i = \alpha$, $\beta_j = \beta$ say. Equation 6.5.1 now becomes

$$\sum_i \sum_j (\alpha_i^* + \beta_j^*)(\mu + \alpha + \beta) = 0$$

for *every* α_i^* and β_j^* satisfying the constraints $\sum u_i \alpha_i^* = \sum v_j \beta_j^* = 0$. Since we are concerned with nontrivial vectors $(\mu + \alpha + \beta) \neq 0$, and by putting the $\{\beta_j^*\}$ equal to zero we see that $\sum_i \alpha_i^* = 0$. In the same way $\sum_j \beta_j^* = 0$; we have therefore shown that the identifiability constraints must take the form $\sum_i \alpha_i = 0$ and $\sum_j \beta_j = 0$.

(b) *Sufficiency*. If $\sum_i \alpha_i = \sum_j \beta_j = 0$, then the vector space $\omega_1^\perp \cap \Omega$ is defined by the set of θ_{ij} such that

$$\begin{aligned} 0 &= \sum_i \sum_j (\mu^* + \beta_j^*)(\mu + \alpha_i + \beta_j) \\ &= \mu^*(IJ\mu) + J\sum_j \beta_j \beta_j^*, \end{aligned}$$

for every μ^* and β_j^*. Hence $\mu = 0$ and $\beta_j = 0$, giving $\theta_{ij} = \alpha_i$. This implies that $\omega_1^\perp \cap \Omega \subset \omega_2$ and the proof now follows. The above method of proof was suggested by Dr S.D. Silvey.

We now turn our attention to the least squares estimation of the unknown parameters, and by way of variation we give a slightly different approach from that used in the complete two-way layout.

Let $\sum_i \alpha_i = 0$ and $\sum_j \beta_j = 0$, and consider

$$\begin{aligned} y_{ij} - \theta_{ij} &= (\bar{y}_{..} - \mu) + (\bar{y}_{i.} - \bar{y}_{..} - \alpha_i) + (\bar{y}_{.j} - \bar{y}_{..} - \beta_j) \\ &\quad + (y_{ij} - \bar{y}_{i.} - \bar{y}_{.j} + \bar{y}_{..}). \end{aligned}$$

Squaring both sides, summing on i, j, and using the identifiability constraints, we find that cross-product terms vanish (because of orthogonality) giving

$$\begin{aligned} \sum_i \sum_j (y_{ij} - \theta_{ij})^2 &= IJ(\bar{y}_{..} - \mu)^2 + J\sum_i (\bar{y}_{i.} - \bar{y}_{..} - \alpha_i)^2 \\ &\quad + I\sum_j (\bar{y}_{.j} - \bar{y}_{..} - \beta_j)^2 + \sum_i \sum_j (y_{ij} - \bar{y}_{i.} - \bar{y}_{.j} + \bar{y}_{..})^2. \end{aligned}$$

Thus, minimising $\sum_i \sum_j (y_{ij} - \theta_{ij})^2$ with respect to μ, $\{\alpha_i\}$ and $\{\beta_j\}$ gives least squares estimates

$$\begin{aligned} \mu_0 &= \bar{y}_{..} \\ \alpha_{i0} &= \bar{y}_{i.} - \bar{y}_{..} \\ \beta_{j0} &= \bar{y}_{.j} - \bar{y}_{..} \end{aligned}$$

and these are the same irrespective of whether some of the parameters are put equal to zero. This means that we do not have to recalculate the estimates for testing the hypotheses H_1 and H_2, and the analysis of variance table is as follows:

Table 6.5.2

Source	s.s.	d.f.	m.s.s.
Between treatments	$J \sum_i (\bar{y}_{i.} - \bar{y}_{..})^2$	$I-1$	m.s.s. (1)
Between blocks	$I \sum_j (\bar{y}_{.j} - \bar{y}_{..})^2$	$J-1$	m.s.s. (2)
Residual	$\sum_i \sum_j (y_{ij} - \bar{y}_{i.} - \bar{y}_{.j} + \bar{y}_{..})^2$	$(I-1)(J-1)$	m.s.s. (r)
Corrected total	$\sum_i \sum_j (y_{ij} - \bar{y}_{..})^2$	$IJ-1$	
Correction for mean	$IJ\bar{y}_{..}^2$	1	
Total	$\sum_i \sum_j y_{ij}^2$	IJ	

The test statistic for testing H_p $(p = 1, 2,)$ is simply

$$F = \frac{\text{m.s.s. } (p)}{\text{m.s.s. } (r)}$$

Before concluding this section, let us consider the model

$$y_{ijk**} = \mu + \alpha_i + \beta_j + \tau_k + \ldots\ldots + e_{ijk**}$$

with identifiability constraints $\sum_i u_i \alpha_i = \sum_j v_j \beta_j = \sum_k w_k \tau_k = \ldots = 0$. The hypotheses of interest are H_1 : all the $\{\alpha_i\}$ zero, H_2 : all the $\{\beta_j\}$ zero, etc., and we add the hypothesis $H_0 : \mu = 0$. As the proof of theorem 6.5.1 can be generalized to deal with this model, we have that the hypotheses $H_0, H_1, H_2, \ldots$ are orthogonal with respect to G, the hypothesis of no interactions, if and only if the identifiability constraints take the form $\sum_i \alpha_i = \sum_j \beta_j = \sum_k \tau_k = \ldots = 0$. The Latin and hyper-Latin squares and factorial designs with no interactions are obviously special cases of this general model.

6.6 Orthogonal polynomials

Suppose we have a polynomial regression model

$$E[y_i] = \beta_0 + \beta_1 x_i + \ldots + \beta_p x_i^p, \quad i = 1, 2, \ldots, n.$$

In §6.1 we discussed the method of making an approximate fit of the form

$$E[y_i] = \beta_0 + \beta_1 x_i + \dots + \beta_k x^k$$

and then testing a sequence of nested hypotheses $\beta_k = 0$, $\beta_k = \beta_{k-1} = 0$, etc. The main disadvantage of this method is that the least squares estimates of the $\{\beta_i\}$ have to be recalculated at each stage of the nesting. However, the algebra would be much simpler if each of the hypotheses $H_i : \beta_i = 0$, $i = 0, 1, 2, \dots, k$ were orthogonal, for then the least squares estimates β_{i0} would be uncorrelated, that is $\text{cov}(\beta_{i0}, \beta_{j0}) = 0$ for $i \neq j$, and would be the same irrespective of whether some of the $\{\beta_i\}$ were made zero. This means that there would be no need to recalculate these estimates at each stage. One method of achieving this desired simplification is by the use of orthogonal polynomials. It amounts to transforming from the set of parameters $\{\beta_i\}$ to a new set of parameters $\{\gamma_i\}$ say, such that the hypotheses $H_i : \gamma_i = 0$ $(i = 0, 1, \dots, k)$ are orthogonal and $\beta_k = \beta_{k-1} = \dots = \beta_i = 0$ if and only if $\gamma_k = \gamma_{k-1} = \dots = \gamma_i = 0$ for every i. For a discussion on the method and use of orthogonal polynomials see Plackett (1960a, Chapter 6), Kendall and Stuart (1961), or Graybill (1961).

6.7 The use of component analysis in regression

Suppose we have a regression model

$$E[y_i] = \beta_1 x_{i1} + \beta_2 x_{i2} + \dots + \beta_p x_{ip} \qquad i = 1, 2, \dots, n,$$

and let $\mathbf{X} = (\mathbf{x}_1, \mathbf{x}_2, \dots, \mathbf{x}_p)'$ where

$$\mathbf{x}_i' = (x_{i1}, x_{i2}, \dots, x_{ip}).$$

If $\boldsymbol{\beta}' = (\beta_1, \beta_2, \dots, \beta_p)$ then $E[\mathbf{y}] = \mathbf{X}\boldsymbol{\beta}$. Assuming that $\mathbf{X}$ has rank p then $D[\boldsymbol{\beta}_0] = \sigma^2(\mathbf{X}'\mathbf{X})^{-1}$ where $\boldsymbol{\beta}_0$ is the least squares estimate of $\boldsymbol{\beta}$ (§3.4). Since $\mathbf{X}'\mathbf{X}$ is symmetric there exists an orthogonal matrix $\mathbf{T} = (\mathbf{t}_1, \mathbf{t}_2, \dots, \mathbf{t}_p)$ such that $\mathbf{T}'\mathbf{X}'\mathbf{X}\mathbf{T} = \text{diag}(\lambda_1, \lambda_2, \dots, \lambda_p)$ where $\lambda_1, \lambda_2, \dots, \lambda_p$ are the eigen values of $\mathbf{X}'\mathbf{X}$.

Suppose now we make the transformation

$$z_{ij} = \mathbf{x}_i'\mathbf{t}_j \text{ for } i = 1, 2, \dots, n, \text{ and } j = 1, 2, \dots, p,$$

and let $\mathbf{Z} = [(z_{ij})]$; then

$$\mathbf{Z} = \mathbf{X}\mathbf{T}.$$

Hence

$$\begin{aligned}\mathbf{X}\boldsymbol{\beta} &= \mathbf{X}\mathbf{T}\mathbf{T}'\boldsymbol{\beta} \\ &= \mathbf{X}\mathbf{T}\boldsymbol{\gamma}, \text{ say,} \\ &= \mathbf{Z}\boldsymbol{\gamma}\end{aligned}$$

and

$$\begin{aligned} D[\boldsymbol{\gamma}_0] &= \sigma^2(\mathbf{Z}'\mathbf{Z})^{-1} \\ &= \sigma^2(\mathbf{T}'\mathbf{X}'\mathbf{X}\mathbf{T})^{-1} \\ &= \sigma^2 \operatorname{diag}(\lambda_1^{-1}, \ldots, \lambda_p^{-1}). \end{aligned}$$

This last result shows that the least squares estimates γ_{i0} of γ_i $(i = 1, 2, \ldots, p)$ are uncorrelated and therefore the hypotheses $H_i : \gamma_i = 0$ $(i = 1, 2, \ldots, k)$ are orthogonal. Thus instead of carrying out a regression analysis on the model $E[\mathbf{y}] = \mathbf{X}\boldsymbol{\beta}$ in which we have to recalculate the least squares estimates of the $\{\beta_i\}$ every time an element β_j is put equal to zero, we can use the model $E[\mathbf{y}] = \mathbf{Z}\boldsymbol{\gamma}$ where the least squares estimates of the $\{\gamma_i\}$ remain unchanged throughout. Of course one has to calculate the eigen vectors $\mathbf{t}_1, \ldots, \mathbf{t}_p$ to obtain $\mathbf{Z}$, and the eigen values λ_i to obtain $D[\boldsymbol{\gamma}_0]$. A quick method of doing this is given in Kendall (1957, Chapter 2). This technique of extracting the eigen vectors is known as component analysis (cf. Anderson, 1958, Chapter 11).

6.8 Non-orthogonal hypotheses

In two-factor complete layouts with unequal observations per cell, the property of orthogonality breaks down when the numbers of observations do not satisfy the proportionality conditions of theorem 6.3.1. Without orthogonality one finds that there is a considerable increase in computation, especially in the solving of the linear least squares equations (cf. Scheffé, § 4.4 and Rao, 1952, § 3e). However, if the numbers of observations per cell are not too different one approach is to assume that there are equal numbers per cell and use the method of missing observations described in Chapter 8. Of course the hypotheses would still remain non-orthogonal, and one would use some nested procedure for splitting up the sums of squares. Another possible approach is to treat one of the factors as a concomitant variable and carry out an analysis of covariance using the methods of Chapter 7 (Quenouille, 1948). Finally, one can use approximate methods of analysis, and the reader is referred to Kramer (1955) for details.

Non-orthogonal hypotheses also occur in incomplete block designs; however, in this case the order of nesting the hypotheses is fixed, as one is primarily interested in tests concerning the treatment differences rather than the block differences. A general discussion on block designs is given in Tocher (1952) where he is concerned mainly with estimating the treatments and not just the treatment differences as we have considered in §6.5. His model is

$$\theta_{ij} = \tau_i + \beta_j, \quad \text{where} \quad \sum_j \beta_j = 0 \quad \text{and} \quad \tau_i = \mu + \alpha_i$$

and the various types of designs arise as one considers variations in the dispersion matrix $D[\boldsymbol{\tau}_0]$ of the least squares estimate $\boldsymbol{\tau}_0$ of $\boldsymbol{\tau} = (\tau_1, \tau_2, \ldots, \tau_I)'$. An alternative method of classification based on the inverse of $D[\boldsymbol{\tau}_0]$ is given by Pearce (1963).

6.9 Additional references

For a further discussion on the use of the nested method cf. Hogg (1961, 1962) and Seber (1964b).

There are many references on experimental design, which may be classified as follows:–

Mathematical: Chakrabarti (1962), Graybill (1961), Kempthorne (1952), Mann (1949), Plackett (1960), and Scheffé (1959).

Methodological: Cochran and Cox (1957), Davies (1954), Federer (1955), Hicks (1964), Quenouille (1953), Winer (1962), and Yates (1937).

General: Cox (1958), Finney (1955), Fisher (1960), and Wilson (1952).

A summary of different analysis of variance models is given by Plackett (1960b).

A general discussion on regression analysis is given in Williams (1959), and Graybill (1961).

CHAPTER 7

MODIFIED HYPOTHESES

7.1 Least squares estimation

Suppose our linear model $G : E[\mathbf{y}] \in \Omega$ is modified to $\widetilde{G} : E[\mathbf{y}] \in \widetilde{\Omega} = \Omega \oplus R[\mathbf{Z}]$, giving

$$\mathbf{y} = \boldsymbol{\theta} + \mathbf{Z}\boldsymbol{\gamma} + \mathbf{e},$$

where $\mathbf{e}$ is $\mathcal{N}[\mathbf{0}, \sigma^2\mathbf{I}]$, $\Omega \cap R[\mathbf{Z}] = \mathbf{0}$, and $\mathbf{Z}$ has linearly independent columns. Instead of calculating the least squares estimates for $\boldsymbol{\theta}$ and $\boldsymbol{\gamma}$ in the new model $\widetilde{G}$, it is often more convenient – especially when the dimension of $R[\mathbf{Z}]$ is small and G has readily obtainable least squares estimates – to obtain least squares estimates for G first and then modify them to give the estimates for $\widetilde{G}$. Suppose $\widetilde{\boldsymbol{\theta}}_0$ and $\widetilde{\boldsymbol{\gamma}}_0$ are the least squares estimates for $\widetilde{G}$, then

$$\widetilde{\boldsymbol{\theta}}_0 + \mathbf{Z}\widetilde{\boldsymbol{\gamma}}_0 = \widetilde{\mathbf{P}}_0\mathbf{y}. \tag{7.1.1}$$

Let $\widetilde{\mathbf{Q}}_0 = \mathbf{I} - \widetilde{\mathbf{P}}_0$ and $\mathbf{Q}_0 = \mathbf{I} - \mathbf{P}_0$; then since $\widetilde{\Omega}^\perp \subset \Omega^\perp$ it follows from lemma 4.4.1 that $\mathbf{Q}_0 - \widetilde{\mathbf{Q}}_0$ is the projection on $\widetilde{\Omega} \cap \Omega^\perp$. But from lemma 4.4.2, equation (4.4.1),

$$\begin{aligned} \widetilde{\Omega} \cap \Omega^\perp &= [\Omega \oplus R[\mathbf{Z}]] \cap \Omega^\perp, \\ &= R[\mathbf{Q}_0\mathbf{Z}]. \end{aligned}$$

Since $R[\mathbf{Z}] \cap \Omega = \mathbf{0}$ we have from lemmas 4.4.3 and 4.4.1

$$\widetilde{\mathbf{P}}_0 - \mathbf{P}_0 = \mathbf{Q}_0\mathbf{Z}(\mathbf{Z}'\mathbf{Q}_0\mathbf{Z})^{-1}\mathbf{Z}'\mathbf{Q}_0. \tag{7.1.2}$$

Premultiplying equation (7.1.1) by $\mathbf{Z}'\mathbf{Q}_0$ and using $\mathbf{Q}_0\widetilde{\boldsymbol{\theta}}_0 = \mathbf{0}$ gives

$$\begin{aligned} \mathbf{Z}'\mathbf{Q}_0\mathbf{Z}\widetilde{\boldsymbol{\gamma}}_0 &= \mathbf{Z}'\mathbf{Q}_0\widetilde{\mathbf{P}}_0\mathbf{y} \\ &= \mathbf{Z}'\mathbf{Q}_0(\mathbf{P}_0 + \mathbf{Q}_0\mathbf{Z}(\mathbf{Z}'\mathbf{Q}_0\mathbf{Z})^{-1}\mathbf{Z}'\mathbf{Q}_0)\mathbf{y} \\ &= \mathbf{Z}'\mathbf{Q}_0\mathbf{y}. \end{aligned}$$

Thus

$$\widetilde{\boldsymbol{\gamma}}_0 = (\mathbf{Z}'\mathbf{Q}_0\mathbf{Z})^{-1}\mathbf{Z}'\mathbf{Q}_0\mathbf{y} \tag{7.1.3}$$

and

$$\begin{aligned}\tilde{\boldsymbol{\theta}}_0 &= \tilde{\mathbf{P}}_0\mathbf{y} - \mathbf{Z}\tilde{\boldsymbol{\gamma}}_0 \\ &= (\mathbf{P}_0 + \mathbf{Q}_0\mathbf{Z}(\mathbf{Z}'\mathbf{Q}_0\mathbf{Z})^{-1}\mathbf{Z}'\mathbf{Q}_0 - \mathbf{Z}(\mathbf{Z}'\mathbf{Q}_0\mathbf{Z})^{-1}\mathbf{Z}'\mathbf{Q}_0)\mathbf{y} \\ &= \mathbf{P}_0(\mathbf{y} - \mathbf{Z}\tilde{\boldsymbol{\gamma}}_0). \qquad (7.1.4)\end{aligned}$$

This approach is a slight generalisation of that given by Scheffé (§ 6.2). In practice one can obtain these estimates by a two-stage least squares procedure as follows.

We first of all assume $\boldsymbol{\gamma} = \mathbf{0}$ and obtain $\boldsymbol{\theta}_0 = \mathbf{P}_0\mathbf{y}$ and the residual $\mathbf{y}'\mathbf{Q}_0\mathbf{y}$. Now minimising $(\mathbf{y}-\mathbf{Z}\boldsymbol{\gamma})'\mathbf{Q}_0(\mathbf{y}-\mathbf{Z}\boldsymbol{\gamma})$ with respect to $\boldsymbol{\gamma}$ gives the least squares equations (cf. equation (3.4.1))

$$-\mathbf{Z}'\mathbf{Q}_0\mathbf{y} + \mathbf{Z}'\mathbf{Q}_0\mathbf{Z}\tilde{\boldsymbol{\gamma}}_0 = \mathbf{0}$$

or

$$\tilde{\boldsymbol{\gamma}}_0 = (\mathbf{Z}'\mathbf{Q}_0\mathbf{Z})^{-1}\mathbf{Z}'\mathbf{Q}_0\mathbf{y}$$

as above. The estimate $\boldsymbol{\theta}_0$ is obtained by replacing $\mathbf{y}$ by $\mathbf{y} - \mathbf{Z}\tilde{\boldsymbol{\gamma}}_0$ in $\boldsymbol{\theta}_0$ (cf. equation (7.1.4)); the correct residual s.s. is simply the minimum of $(\mathbf{y}-\mathbf{Z}\boldsymbol{\gamma})'\mathbf{Q}_0(\mathbf{y}-\mathbf{Z}\boldsymbol{\gamma})$, as

$$\begin{aligned}(\mathbf{y}-\mathbf{Z}\tilde{\boldsymbol{\gamma}}_0)'\mathbf{Q}_0(\mathbf{y}-\mathbf{Z}\tilde{\boldsymbol{\gamma}}_0) &= \mathbf{y}'(\mathbf{Q}_0 - \mathbf{Q}_0\mathbf{Z}(\mathbf{Z}'\mathbf{Q}_0\mathbf{Z})^{-1}\mathbf{Z}'\mathbf{Q}_0)\mathbf{y} \\ &= \mathbf{y}'\tilde{\mathbf{Q}}_0\mathbf{y}.\end{aligned}$$

EXERCISE 11: Prove that $\tilde{\boldsymbol{\gamma}}_0$ and $\boldsymbol{\theta}_0$ are statistically independent.

7.2 Hypothesis testing

One of the first hypotheses of interest is $H_\gamma : \boldsymbol{\gamma} = \mathbf{0}$ and the F statistic for testing this is given by

$$F = \frac{n - \dim[\tilde{\Omega}]}{\dim[R[\mathbf{Z}]]} \cdot \frac{\mathbf{y}'(\tilde{\mathbf{P}}_0 - \mathbf{P}_0)\mathbf{y}}{\mathbf{y}'(\mathbf{I} - \tilde{\mathbf{P}}_0)\mathbf{y}}.$$

Using equations (7.1.2) and (7.1.3), we have the following alternative expressions:

$$\begin{aligned}\mathbf{y}'(\tilde{\mathbf{P}}_0 - \mathbf{P}_0)\mathbf{y} &= \mathbf{y}'\mathbf{Q}_0\mathbf{Z}(\mathbf{Z}'\mathbf{Q}_0\mathbf{Z})^{-1}\mathbf{Z}'\mathbf{Q}_0\mathbf{y} \\ &= \tilde{\boldsymbol{\gamma}}_0'(\mathbf{Z}'\mathbf{Q}_0\mathbf{y})\end{aligned}$$

and

$$\mathbf{y}'\tilde{\mathbf{Q}}_0\mathbf{y} = \mathbf{y}'\mathbf{Q}_0\mathbf{y} - \tilde{\boldsymbol{\gamma}}_0'(\mathbf{Z}'\mathbf{Q}_0\mathbf{y})$$

which can be used for performing the calculations.

If the test is not significant, we can accept the hypothesis and we are back to our usual model G. However, if the test is significant, we would then test some other hypothesis of the form $\tilde{H} : E[\mathbf{y}] \in \tilde{\omega} =$

$\omega \oplus R[\mathbf{Z}]$ where $\omega \subset \Omega$, and repeat the method given above for finding the least squares estimates $\tilde{\boldsymbol{\theta}}_1$ and $\tilde{\boldsymbol{\gamma}}_1$. The F statistic would then be

$$F = \left(\frac{n - \dim[\tilde{\Omega}]}{\dim[\Omega] - \dim[\omega]}\right)\left(\frac{\mathbf{y}'(\tilde{\mathbf{P}}_0 - \tilde{\mathbf{P}}_1)\mathbf{y}}{\mathbf{y}'(\mathbf{I} - \tilde{\mathbf{P}}_0)\mathbf{y}}\right)$$

where

$$\tilde{\boldsymbol{\theta}}_1 + \mathbf{Z}\tilde{\boldsymbol{\gamma}}_1 = \tilde{\mathbf{P}}_1\mathbf{y}.$$

7.3 Analysis of covariance

The above modified hypothesis technique of §7.1 is used in the analysis of covariance where the underlying model takes the form $E[\mathbf{y}] = \mathbf{X}\boldsymbol{\beta} + \mathbf{Z}\boldsymbol{\gamma}$, with identifiability constraints $\mathbf{H}\boldsymbol{\beta} = \mathbf{0}$. This model is a mixture of the analysis of variance model $\boldsymbol{\theta} = \mathbf{X}\boldsymbol{\beta}$ where the elements of $\mathbf{X}$ are zero or 1 and the underlying factors enter *qualitatively*, and a regression model $\boldsymbol{\theta} = \mathbf{Z}\boldsymbol{\gamma}$ where $\mathbf{Z}$ is of full rank and the factors are *quantitative*. We then have (example 2, §3.4)

$$\mathbf{P}_0 = \mathbf{X}(\mathbf{X}'\mathbf{X} + \mathbf{H}'\mathbf{H})^{-1}\mathbf{X}'$$

and from equation (7.1.4)

$$\begin{aligned}\tilde{\boldsymbol{\beta}}_0 &= (\mathbf{X}'\mathbf{X} + \mathbf{H}'\mathbf{H})^{-1}\mathbf{X}'\tilde{\boldsymbol{\theta}}_0 \\ &= (\mathbf{X}'\mathbf{X} + \mathbf{H}'\mathbf{H})^{-1}\mathbf{X}'(\mathbf{y} - \mathbf{Z}\tilde{\boldsymbol{\gamma}}_0)\end{aligned}$$

which simply amounts to replacing $\mathbf{y}$ by $\mathbf{y} - \mathbf{Z}\tilde{\boldsymbol{\gamma}}_0$ in $\boldsymbol{\beta}_0$. To demonstrate the two-stage least squares method we consider the following example.

Suppose we have a randomised blocks design with I treatments and J blocks and let y_{ij} be the observation on the ith treatment applied to the jth block. The assumption G is assumed to take the form $E[y_{ij}] = \mu + \alpha_i + \beta_j$ where $\sum_i \alpha_i = 0$ and $\sum_j \beta_j = 0$ are the identifiability constraints. In order to explain the variation in y_{ij} with respect to i and j, observations on another variable z_{ij} are taken and we assume the model $\tilde{G} : E[y_{ij}] = \mu + \alpha_i + \beta_j + \gamma z_{ij}$. For example, in an agricultural experiment carried out in a sandy area, the treatments may refer to different fertilizers, the blocks to strips of land, and z_{ij} is a measure of the sand content in the i, jth plot. The variable z is known as a *concomitant* variable, and it is assumed that the values of z are not affected by the treatments. The vector $\boldsymbol{\beta}$ mentioned at the beginning of this section is given by $\boldsymbol{\beta}' = (\mu, \alpha_1, \ldots, \alpha_I, \beta_1, \ldots, \beta_J)$ and $\boldsymbol{\gamma}$ is the single element γ.

Consider the following table (cf. Table 6.5.2).

Source	d.f.	s.s. (y, y)	s.s.(y,z)	s.s.(z,z)
Blocks	$J-1$	$I\sum_j(\bar{y}_{.j}-\bar{y}_{..})^2 = B_{yy}$	B_{yz}	B_{zz}
Treatments	$I-1$	$J\sum_i(\bar{y}_{i.}-\bar{y}_{..})^2 = T_{yy}$	T_{yz}	T_{zz}
Residual	$(I-1)(J-1)$	$\sum_i\sum_j(y_{ij}-\bar{y}_{i.}-\bar{y}_{.j}+\bar{y}_{..})^2 = R_{yy}$	R_{yz}	R_{zz}
Total	$IJ-1$	$\sum_i\sum_j(y_{ij}-\bar{y}_{..})^2 = S_{yy}$	S_{yz}	S_{zz}

The residual s.s. for the model with $\gamma = 0$ is

$$R_{yy} = \sum_i\sum_j(y_{ij}-\bar{y}_{i.}-\bar{y}_{.j}+\bar{y}_{..})^2 .$$

We now replace y_{ij} by $y_{ij}-\gamma z_{ij}$ in R_{yy}, giving

$$\sum_i\sum_j\{(y_{ij}-\gamma z_{ij})-(\bar{y}_{i.}-\gamma\bar{z}_{i.})-(\bar{y}_{.j}-\gamma\bar{z}_{.j})+(\bar{y}_{..}-\gamma\bar{z}_{..})\}^2$$

$$= \sum_i\sum_j\{(y_{ij}-\bar{y}_{i.}-\bar{y}_{.j}+\bar{y}_{..})-\gamma(z_{ij}-\bar{z}_{i.}-\bar{z}_{.j}+\bar{z}_{..})\}^2$$

$$= R_{yy} - 2\gamma R_{yz} + \gamma^2 R_{zz} . \qquad (7.3.1)$$

Minimising this with respect to γ gives

$$\tilde{\gamma}_0 = R_{yz}/R_{zz} ,$$

the least squares estimate of γ for $\tilde{G}$. The residual $\mathbf{y}'\tilde{\mathbf{Q}}_0\mathbf{y}$ is obtained by inserting $\tilde{\gamma}_0$ in (7.3.1) giving $R_{yy} - R_{yz}^2/R_{zz}$ with $(I-1)(J-1)-1$ degrees of freedom. To test the hypothesis $H_\gamma : \gamma = 0$ we use

$$F = \frac{[(I-1)(J-1)-1]}{1} \cdot \frac{R_{yz}^2/R_{zz}}{R_{yy} - R_{yz}^2/R_{zz}} .$$

The main hypothesis of interest is that there are no differences in the treatments, that is

$$\alpha_1 = \alpha_2 = \dots = \alpha_I = 0 \quad \text{or} \quad \tilde{H}_1 : E[y_{ij}] = \mu + \beta_j + \gamma z_{ij} .$$

Our sums of squares table now becomes

Source	d.f.	s.s.(y,y)	s.s.(y,z)	s.s.(z,z)
Blocks	$J-1$	B_{yy}	B_{yz}	B_{zz}
Residual	$J(I-1)$	$R_{yy}+T_{yy}$	$R_{yz}+T_{yz}$	$R_{zz}+T_{zz}$
Total	$IJ-1$	S_{yy}	S_{yz}	S_{zz}

By a similar algebra to that above we can show that the residual is

$$\mathbf{y}'\widetilde{\mathbf{Q}}_1\mathbf{y} = R_{yy} + T_{yy} - (R_{yz} + T_{yz})^2/(R_{zz} + T_{zz}).$$

To test $\widetilde{H}_1$ the numerator s.s. of the F test is thus

$$\mathbf{y}'(\widetilde{\mathbf{Q}}_1 - \widetilde{\mathbf{Q}}_0)\mathbf{y} = T_{yy} + R_{yz}^2/R_{zz} - (R_{yz} + T_{yz})^2/(R_{zz} + T_{zz})$$

and we can now construct an analysis of variance table giving the decomposition of the total s.s., S_{yy}.

Source	d.f.	s.s.
Blocks (ignoring regression and treatments)	$J-1$	B_{yy}
Regression (allowing for blocks, ignoring treatments)	1	$\dfrac{(R_{yz} + T_{yz})^2}{(R_{zz} + T_{zz})}$
Treatments (allowing for blocks and regression)	$I-1$	$T_{yy} - \dfrac{(R_{yz} + T_{yz})^2}{(R_{zz} + T_{zz})} + \dfrac{R_{yz}^2}{R_{zz}}$
Residual	$(I-1)(J-1)-1$	$R_{yy} - R_{yz}^2/R_{zz}$
Total	$IJ-1$	$S_{yy} = B_{yy} + T_{yy} + R_{yy}$

We note that these sums of squares correspond to the numerator sums of squares for testing the following sequence of nested hypotheses.

Hypothesis	s.s.
$\widetilde{H}_1 \wedge H_\gamma \wedge H_2 \;:\; \theta_{ij} = \mu$	$\mathbf{y}'(\mathbf{P}_1 - \mathbf{P}_{12})\mathbf{y}$
$\widetilde{H}_1 \wedge H_\gamma \;:\; \theta_{ij} = \mu + \beta_j$	$\mathbf{y}'(\widetilde{\mathbf{P}}_1 - \mathbf{P}_1)\mathbf{y}$
$\widetilde{H}_1 \;:\; \theta_{ij} = \mu + \beta_j + \gamma z_{ij}$	$\mathbf{y}'(\widetilde{\mathbf{P}}_0 - \widetilde{\mathbf{P}}_1)\mathbf{y}$
$\widetilde{G} \;:\; \theta_{ij} = \mu + \alpha_i + \beta_j + \gamma z_{ij}$	$\mathbf{y}'(\mathbf{I} - \widetilde{\mathbf{P}}_0)\mathbf{y}$
Total	$\mathbf{y}'(\mathbf{I} - \mathbf{P}_{12})\mathbf{y}$

Here H_2 is the hypothesis that the block effects $\{\beta_i\}$ are zero and

$\widetilde{H}_1 \wedge H_\gamma \wedge H_2$ ($= H_1 \wedge H_2$) is the hypothesis that $\theta_{ij} = \mu$, or $\boldsymbol{\theta} \in \omega_1 \cap \omega_2$, say. The matrices $\mathbf{P}_1$ and $\mathbf{P}_{12}$ represent projections on ω_1 and $\omega_1 \cap \omega_2$ respectively.

If the test for $\widetilde{H}_1$ is significant and therefore appreciable differences in the treatments do exist, we would then be interested in the least squares estimates $\{\widetilde{\alpha}_{i0}\}$ of the main treatment effects. To obtain these estimates we simply replace y_{ij} by $(y_{ij} - \widetilde{\gamma}_0 z_{ij})$ in $\alpha_{i0} = \bar{y}_{i.} - \bar{y}_{..}$, giving

$$\widetilde{\alpha}_{i0} = \bar{y}_{i.} - \bar{y}_{..} - \widetilde{\gamma}_0(\bar{z}_{i.} - \bar{z}_{..}).$$

To find confidence intervals for any contrast $\phi = \sum_i c_i \alpha_i$, where $\sum_i c_i = 0$, we require its least squares estimate

$$\widetilde{\phi}_0 = \sum_i c_i \widetilde{\alpha}_{i0} = \sum_i c_i (\bar{y}_{i.} - \widetilde{\gamma}_0 \bar{z}_{i.})$$

and the variance of this estimate. Since $\widetilde{\gamma}_0$ is statistically independent of α_{i0} (exercise 11, §7.1)

$$\text{var}[\widetilde{\phi}_0] = \sum_i c_i^2 \sigma^2/J + (\sum_i c_i \bar{z}_{i.})^2 \text{var}[\widetilde{\gamma}_0],$$

where

$$\begin{aligned} \text{var}[\widetilde{\gamma}_0] &= \text{var}[R_{yz}/R_{zz}] \\ &= \text{var}[(y_{ij} - \bar{y}_{i.} - \bar{y}_{.j} + \bar{y}_{..})]/R_{zz}. \end{aligned}$$

Now $y_{ij} - \bar{y}_{i.} - \bar{y}_{.j} + \bar{y}_{..} = \mathbf{a}'\mathbf{y}$ and therefore

$$\begin{aligned} \text{var}[\mathbf{a}'\mathbf{y}] &= \sigma^2 \mathbf{a}'\mathbf{a} \\ &= \sigma^2 \sum_r \sum_s (\delta_{ir}\delta_{js} - \delta_{ir}/J - \delta_{js}/I + 1/IJ)^2 \\ &= \sigma^2 (I-1)(J-1)/IJ. \end{aligned}$$

Also $E[\widetilde{\phi}_0] = \phi$ and therefore $\widetilde{\phi}_0 - \phi$ is $\mathcal{N}[0, \sigma^2 v]$ where

$$v = \sum_i c_i^2/J + (\sum_i c_i \bar{z}_{i.})^2 (I-1)(J-1)/R_{zz} IJ.$$

If

$$s^2 = \mathbf{y}'(\mathbf{I} - \widetilde{\mathbf{P}}_0)\mathbf{y}/\{(I-1)(J-1) - 1\}$$

then we can obtain confidence intervals for ϕ from $(\widetilde{\phi}_0 - \phi)/s\sqrt{(v)}$ which has the t distribution with $(I-1)(J-1) - 1$ degrees of freedom.

7.4 Addition of extra variables in regression

Consider the regression model $y_i = \sum_{j=1}^{p} x_{ij}\beta_j + e_i$ with matrix representation $\mathbf{y} = \mathbf{X}\boldsymbol{\beta} + \mathbf{e}$. Then the least squares estimate $\boldsymbol{\beta}_0$ is given by

$$\boldsymbol{\beta}_0 = (\mathbf{X}'\mathbf{X})^{-1}\mathbf{X}'\mathbf{y} \quad \text{and}$$
$$D[\boldsymbol{\beta}_0] = \sigma^2(\mathbf{X}'\mathbf{X})^{-1}.$$

Suppose we wish to introduce a further unknown parameter β_{p+1} corresponding to $\mathbf{x}'_{p+1} = (x_{1,p+1}, x_{2,p+1}, \ldots, x_{n,p+1})$ giving the modified model $\mathbf{y} = \mathbf{X}\boldsymbol{\beta} + \mathbf{x}_{p+1}\beta_{p+1} + \mathbf{e}$. If $\boldsymbol{\beta}_0$ has already been calculated, it is simpler to modify $\boldsymbol{\beta}_0$ as in the analysis of covariance above than to recalculate the least squares estimate of $\boldsymbol{\beta}$. In this example $\widetilde{\Omega} = R[\mathbf{X}] \oplus R[\mathbf{x}_{p+1}]$ and therefore, from equation (7.1.3),

$$\widetilde{\beta}_{p+1,0} = (\mathbf{x}'_{p+1}\mathbf{Q}_0\mathbf{x}_{p+1})^{-1}\mathbf{x}'_{p+1}\mathbf{Q}_0\mathbf{y},$$

where $\mathbf{Q}_0 = \mathbf{I} - \mathbf{X}(\mathbf{X}'\mathbf{X})^{-1}\mathbf{X}'$. From equation (7.1.4) it is seen that our modified estimate of $\boldsymbol{\beta}$ is given by

$$\begin{aligned}\widetilde{\boldsymbol{\beta}}_0 &= (\mathbf{X}'\mathbf{X})^{-1}\mathbf{X}'\widetilde{\boldsymbol{\theta}}_0 \\ &= (\mathbf{X}'\mathbf{X})^{-1}\mathbf{X}'(\mathbf{y} - \mathbf{x}_{p+1}\widetilde{\beta}_{p+1,0}).\end{aligned}$$

Now $\mathrm{var}[\widetilde{\beta}_{p+1,0}] = \sigma^2(\mathbf{x}'_{p+1}\mathbf{Q}_0\mathbf{x}_{p+1})^{-1} = m$, say, and since $\mathbf{Q}_0\mathbf{X} = \mathbf{0}$,

$$\begin{aligned}D[\widetilde{\boldsymbol{\beta}}_0] &= \sigma^2(\mathbf{X}'\mathbf{X})^{-1}\mathbf{X}'[\mathbf{I} + \mathbf{x}_{p+1}(\mathbf{x}'_{p+1}\mathbf{Q}_0\mathbf{x}_{p+1})^{-1}\mathbf{x}'_{p+1}]\mathbf{X}(\mathbf{X}'\mathbf{X})^{-1} \\ &= D[\boldsymbol{\beta}_0] + \mathbf{L}\mathbf{L}'m,\end{aligned}$$

where $\mathbf{L} = (\mathbf{X}'\mathbf{X})^{-1}\mathbf{X}'\mathbf{x}_{p+1}$. Also

$$\begin{aligned}\mathrm{cov}[\widetilde{\beta}_{p+1,0}, \widetilde{\boldsymbol{\beta}}_0] &= (\mathbf{X}'\mathbf{X})^{-1}\mathbf{X}'\mathbf{Q}_0\mathbf{x}_{p+1}\, m - (\mathbf{X}'\mathbf{X})^{-1}\mathbf{X}'\mathbf{x}_{p+1}\, m, \\ &= -\mathbf{L}m.\end{aligned}$$

Thus the dispersion matrix for $\beta_{10}, \beta_{20}, \ldots, \beta_{p+1,0}$ is

$$\begin{bmatrix} (\mathbf{X}'\mathbf{X})^{-1}\sigma^2 + \mathbf{L}\mathbf{L}'m, & -\mathbf{L}m \\ -\mathbf{L}'m, & m \end{bmatrix}$$

and is readily calculated when $(\mathbf{X}'\mathbf{X})^{-1}$ is known. Therefore, instead of having to invert an augmented $(p+1)\times(p+1)$ matrix, we only have to invert the 1×1 matrix $\mathbf{x}'_{p+1}\mathbf{Q}_0\mathbf{x}_{p+1}$.

This method can be readily extended to deal with the problem of introducing, say, t extra variables $\beta_{p+1}, \ldots, \beta_{p+t}$. The dispersion matrix for $\beta_{10}, \ldots, \beta_{p+t,0}$ now becomes

$$\begin{bmatrix} (\mathbf{X}'\mathbf{X})^{-1}\sigma^2 + \mathbf{L}\mathbf{M}\mathbf{L}', & -\mathbf{L}\mathbf{M} \\ -\mathbf{M}\mathbf{L}', & \mathbf{M} \end{bmatrix}$$

where
$$\mathbf{L} = (\mathbf{X}'\mathbf{X})^{-1}\mathbf{X}'(\mathbf{x}_{p+1}, \ldots, \mathbf{x}_{p+t}),$$
$$\mathbf{M} = \sigma^2[(\mathbf{x}_{p+1}, \ldots, \mathbf{x}_{p+t})'\mathbf{Q}_0(\mathbf{x}_{p+1}, \ldots, \mathbf{x}_{p+t})]^{-1}.$$

The above method was first given by Cochran (1939) for the case of one extra variable and extended by Quenouille (1950) for dealing with several extra variables.

CHAPTER 8

MISSING OBSERVATIONS

8.1 Estimation

Suppose that in the general model $\mathbf{y} = \boldsymbol{\theta} + \mathbf{e}$, where $\boldsymbol{\theta} \in \Omega$, we find that m of the n elements of $\mathbf{y}$ are incompletely observed or "lost"; for example, a test-tube may be broken, an animal may die, or a field plot may be trampled. Then by relabelling the y_i we have

$$\mathbf{y} = \begin{bmatrix} \mathbf{y}_{n-m} \\ \mathbf{0} \end{bmatrix} + \begin{bmatrix} \mathbf{0} \\ \mathbf{y}_m \end{bmatrix}$$

$$= \mathbf{y}^{(1)} + \mathbf{y}^{(2)},$$

where only the $n-m$ values $\mathbf{y}_{n-m}$ are observed. Thus we can write E_n as the direct sum of two vector spaces V_1 and V_2, that is $E_n = V_1 \oplus V_2$ and $\mathbf{y}^{(i)} = \mathbf{P}^{(i)}\mathbf{y}$, where $\mathbf{P}^{(i)}$ represents the orthogonal projection of E_n on V_i. Let $\Omega_i \equiv \mathbf{P}^{(i)}\Omega$ and $E[\mathbf{y}^{(i)}] = \boldsymbol{\theta}^{(i)} = \mathbf{P}^{(i)}\boldsymbol{\theta}$. Then $\Omega_1 \perp \Omega_2$ and in general $\Omega \neq \Omega_1 \oplus \Omega_2$, although $\Omega \subset \Omega_1 \oplus \Omega_2$. Also $\dim[\Omega_i] \leqslant \dim[\Omega]$.

To find the least squares estimates we first of all minimise $(\mathbf{y}^{(1)} - \boldsymbol{\theta}^{(1)})'(\mathbf{y}^{(1)} - \boldsymbol{\theta}^{(1)}) + (\mathbf{y}^{(2)} - \boldsymbol{\theta}^{(2)})'(\mathbf{y}^{(2)} - \boldsymbol{\theta}^{(2)})$, subject to $\boldsymbol{\theta} \in \Omega$, to give $\boldsymbol{\theta}_0$ and then minimise this minimum s.s. with respect to $\mathbf{y}^{(2)}$ to obtain least squares estimates $\mathbf{y}_0^{(2)}$ of the missing observations. Thus

$$\boldsymbol{\theta}_0 = \boldsymbol{\theta}_0^{(1)} + \boldsymbol{\theta}_0^{(2)}$$

$$= \mathbf{P}_0(\mathbf{y}^{(1)} + \mathbf{y}_0^{(2)})$$

and

$$\boldsymbol{\theta}_0^{(2)} = \mathbf{y}_0^{(2)}.$$

Combining these equations,

$$\boldsymbol{\theta}_0^{(2)} = \mathbf{P}_0^{(2)}\boldsymbol{\theta}_0 = \mathbf{P}_0^{(2)}\mathbf{P}_0(\mathbf{y}^{(1)} + \boldsymbol{\theta}_0^{(2)}), \tag{8.1.1}$$

where $\mathbf{P}_0$ and $\mathbf{P}_0^{(i)}$ represent the projections on Ω and Ω_i. We now ask under what conditions equation (8.1.1) has a unique solution for $\boldsymbol{\theta}_0^{(2)}$. To answer this we consider the following equations.

Now

$$\boldsymbol{\theta}_0 = \mathbf{P}_0\boldsymbol{\theta}_0 = \mathbf{P}_0(\boldsymbol{\theta}_0^{(1)} + \theta_0^{(2)}) \tag{8.1.2}$$

and

$$\begin{aligned}\boldsymbol{\theta}_0 &= \mathbf{P}_0(\mathbf{y}^{(1)} + \boldsymbol{\theta}_0^{(2)}) \\ &= \mathbf{P}_0(\mathbf{P}_0^{(1)}\mathbf{y}^{(1)} + \boldsymbol{\theta}_0^{(2)}),\end{aligned} \tag{8.1.3}$$

since $(\mathbf{I} - \mathbf{P}_0^{(1)})\mathbf{y}^{(1)}$ is orthogonal to both Ω_1 and Ω_2 and hence to Ω. Therefore subtracting (8.1.3) from (8.1.2) gives

$$\mathbf{P}_0(\boldsymbol{\theta}_0^{(1)} - \mathbf{P}_0^{(1)}\mathbf{y}^{(1)}) = \mathbf{0}.$$

Thus $\boldsymbol{\theta}_0^{(1)} - \mathbf{P}_0^{(1)}\mathbf{y}^{(1)}$, which belongs to Ω_1, is orthogonal to Ω. This can only happen if

$$\boldsymbol{\theta}_0^{(1)} = \mathbf{P}_0^{(1)}\mathbf{y}^{(1)}$$

and our least squares procedure corresponds to minimising $(\mathbf{y}^{(1)} - \boldsymbol{\theta}^{(1)})'(\mathbf{y}^{(1)} - \boldsymbol{\theta}^{(1)})$, subject to $\boldsymbol{\theta}^{(1)} \in \Omega_1$, and then putting $\mathbf{y}_0^{(2)} = \theta_0^{(2)}$, where $\theta_0^{(2)}$ is chosen such that $\theta_0 = \boldsymbol{\theta}_0^{(1)} + \theta_0^{(2)}$ belongs to Ω. Obviously $\boldsymbol{\theta}_0^{(2)}$ can only be unique if, corresponding to every $\boldsymbol{\theta}^{(1)} \in \Omega_1$, there exists a unique $\boldsymbol{\theta}^{(2)} \in \Omega_2$ such that $\boldsymbol{\theta}^{(1)} + \boldsymbol{\theta}^{(2)} \in \Omega$. Now $\boldsymbol{\theta}^{(2)}$ will be unique if and only if there is no non-zero $\boldsymbol{\phi}^{(2)}$ in Ω_2 such that $(\mathbf{0} + \boldsymbol{\phi}^{(2)}) \in \Omega$, for then $\boldsymbol{\theta}_0^{(2)}$ and $\boldsymbol{\theta}_0^{(2)} + \boldsymbol{\phi}^{(2)}$ both correspond to $\boldsymbol{\theta}_0^{(1)}$. Thus the condition for uniqueness is that

$$\dim[\Omega] = \dim[\Omega_1]$$

and as an exercise we now verify that this condition implies that equation (8.1.1) has a unique solution for $\theta_0^{(2)}$.

Suppose two solutions $\mathbf{u}_1$ and $\mathbf{u}_2$ exist, then

$$\mathbf{u}_1 - \mathbf{u}_2 = \mathbf{P}_0^{(2)}\mathbf{P}_0(\mathbf{u}_1 - \mathbf{u}_2). \tag{8.1.4}$$

Now if $\mathbf{P}_w$ represents the projection on any vector space W, then

$$\mathbf{z} = \mathbf{P}_w\mathbf{z} + (\mathbf{I} - \mathbf{P}_w)\mathbf{z}$$

for every $\mathbf{z}$ and therefore

$$\|\mathbf{z}\| \geqslant \|\mathbf{P}_w\mathbf{z}\|,$$

with equality if and only if $\mathbf{z} \in W$. Applying this twice to equation (8.1.4) gives that $(\mathbf{u}_1 - \mathbf{u}_2) \in \Omega$ and $\mathbf{P}_0(\mathbf{u}_1 - \mathbf{u}_2) \in \Omega_2$. Hence $\mathbf{P}_0(\mathbf{u}_1 - \mathbf{u}_2)$ is in both Ω_2 and Ω; it is therefore zero as $\dim[\Omega] = \dim[\Omega_1]$. But $(\mathbf{u}_1 - \mathbf{u}_2) \in \Omega$ and thus $\mathbf{u}_1 = \mathbf{u}_2$, establishing the uniqueness of $\theta_0^{(2)}$. The above treatment follows Kruskal (1960).

Since $\mathbf{P}_0^{(2)}\theta_0^{(2)} = \theta_0^{(2)}$ we have from equation (8.1.1)

$$\mathbf{P}_0^{(2)}(\mathbf{I}_n - \mathbf{P}_0)\boldsymbol{\theta}_0^{(2)} = \mathbf{P}_0^{(2)}\mathbf{P}_0\mathbf{y}^{(1)} \tag{8.1.5}$$

and therefore only the last m equations of this system are non-trivial as the first $n-m$ rows of $\mathbf{P}_0^{(2)}$ are all zero (lemma 3.3.1). In addition, since $\boldsymbol{\theta}_0^{(2)} = (\mathbf{0}', \mathbf{y}'_{m,0})'$, say, and $\mathbf{P}_0^{(2)}\mathbf{P}_0 = \mathbf{P}^{(2)}\mathbf{P}_0$, we have that

$$(\mathbf{I}_m - \mathbf{T}_0)\,\mathbf{y}_{m,0} = \mathbf{S}_0\mathbf{y}_{n-m} \tag{8.1.6}$$

where

$$\mathbf{P}_0 = \begin{bmatrix} \mathbf{R}_0, & \mathbf{S}_0' \\ \mathbf{S}_0, & \mathbf{T}_0 \end{bmatrix}$$

and $\mathbf{T}_0$ is $m \times m$. Now since $\mathbf{I}_n - \mathbf{P}_0$ is symmetric and idempotent,

$$\mathbf{I}_m - \mathbf{T}_0 = [\mathbf{0}, \mathbf{I}_m][\mathbf{I}_n - \mathbf{P}_0]\begin{bmatrix} \mathbf{0}' \\ \mathbf{I}_m \end{bmatrix},$$

$$= \mathbf{M}\mathbf{M}'$$

where $\mathbf{M} = [\mathbf{0}, \mathbf{I}_m][\mathbf{I}_n - \mathbf{P}_0]$ consists of the last m rows of $\mathbf{I}_n - \mathbf{P}_0$. If the $m \times n$ matrix $\mathbf{M}$ is of rank m, then $\mathbf{M}\mathbf{M}'$ is positive definite, for $\mathbf{x}'\mathbf{M}\mathbf{M}'\mathbf{x} = \mathbf{z}'\mathbf{z} \geqslant 0$ and $\mathbf{z} = \mathbf{M}'\mathbf{x}$ is zero if and only if $\mathbf{x} = \mathbf{0}$. Therefore when $\boldsymbol{\theta}_0^{(2)}$ and hence $\mathbf{y}_{m0}$ is unique, $\mathbf{I}_m - \mathbf{T}_0$ is non-singular and therefore positive definite; the case when $\mathbf{I}_m - \mathbf{T}_0$ is singular is discussed in Wilkinson (1958a and b).

8.2 Hypothesis testing

If we wish to test the hypothesis H that $\theta \in \omega$, a $p{-}q$-dimensional subspace of Ω, then we need to repeat the same procedure as described above to obtain new least squares estimates of $\boldsymbol{\theta}$ for $\boldsymbol{\theta} \in \omega$. The new estimate $\boldsymbol{\theta}_1^{(2)}$ for the missing observations would be given by (cf. equation 8.1.1)

$$\boldsymbol{\theta}_1^{(2)} = \mathbf{P}_1^{(2)}\mathbf{P}_1(\mathbf{y}^{(1)} + \boldsymbol{\theta}_1^{(2)}), \tag{8.2.1}$$

where $\mathbf{P}_1$ and $\mathbf{P}_1^{(i)}$ represent the projection on ω and ω_i ($\equiv \mathbf{P}^{(i)}\omega$) respectively. Once again this equation will have a unique solution if $\dim[\omega] = \dim[\omega_1]$. If $\boldsymbol{\theta}_1^{(2)} = (\mathbf{0}', \mathbf{y}'_{m,1})'$ then

$$(\mathbf{I}_m - \mathbf{T}_1)\,\mathbf{y}_{m,1} = \mathbf{S}_1\mathbf{y}_{n-m}$$

where $\mathbf{T}_1$ consists of the last m rows and columns of $\mathbf{P}_1$.

To calculate the F statistic for testing H, we need to evaluate

$$\mathbf{z}_i'(\mathbf{I}_n - \mathbf{P}_i)\,\mathbf{z}_i = \mathbf{y}^{(1)\prime}(\mathbf{I}_n - \mathbf{P}_i^{(1)})\,\mathbf{y}^{(1)} \tag{8.2.2}$$

for $i = 0, 1$ where $\mathbf{z}_i = \mathbf{y}^{(1)} + \boldsymbol{\theta}_i^{(2)}$. The corresponding degrees of freedom of these sums of squares are $n - p - m$ and $n - p + q - m$ respectively, m degrees of freedom being lost due to the estimation of $\mathbf{y}_m$. Thus

$$F = \frac{n-p-m}{q} \frac{\mathbf{y}^{(1)\prime}(\mathbf{P}_0^{(1)} - \mathbf{P}_1^{(1)})\mathbf{y}^{(1)}}{\mathbf{y}^{(1)\prime}(\mathbf{I}_n - \mathbf{P}_0^{(1)})\mathbf{y}^{(1)}} .$$

8.3 Correction for bias

Instead of calculating $\mathbf{y}^{(1)\prime}(\mathbf{I}_n - \mathbf{P}_1^{(1)})\mathbf{y}^{(1)}$ separately it is often easier to calculate both the numerator and denominator sums of squares using the estimate $\boldsymbol{\theta}_0^{(2)}$ throughout and then applying a so-called " correction for bias", b, to the numerator. Thus from equation (8.2.2)

$$b = \mathbf{z}_0'(\mathbf{I}_n - \mathbf{P}_1)\mathbf{z}_0 - \mathbf{z}_1'(\mathbf{I}_n - \mathbf{P}_1)\mathbf{z}_1$$

and this must be subtracted from $\mathbf{z}_0'(\mathbf{P}_0 - \mathbf{P}_1)\mathbf{z}_0$ to obtain the correct numerator s.s.

Lemma 8.3.1. The bias b is given by

$$b = (\mathbf{z}_0 - \mathbf{z}_1)'(\mathbf{I}_n - \mathbf{P}_1)(\mathbf{z}_0 - \mathbf{z}_1) .$$

Proof. The method of proof is similar to that given by Wilkinson (1958b). From equation (8.2.1),

$$\begin{aligned} \mathbf{P}^{(2)}(\mathbf{I}_n - \mathbf{P}_1)\mathbf{z}_1 &= \boldsymbol{\theta}_1^{(2)} - \mathbf{P}^{(2)}\mathbf{P}_1\mathbf{z}_1 \\ &= \boldsymbol{\theta}_1^{(2)} - \mathbf{P}_1^{(2)}\mathbf{P}_1\mathbf{z}_1 \\ &= \mathbf{0} \end{aligned} \qquad (8.3.1)$$

and therefore

$$\mathbf{P}^{(2)}(\mathbf{I}_n - \mathbf{P}_1)\mathbf{z}_0 = \mathbf{P}^{(2)}(\mathbf{I}_n - \mathbf{P}_1)(\mathbf{z}_0 - \mathbf{z}_1) . \qquad (8.3.2)$$

Now

$$\begin{aligned} b &= \mathbf{z}_0'(\mathbf{I}_n - \mathbf{P}_1)\mathbf{z}_0 - \mathbf{z}_1'(\mathbf{I}_n - \mathbf{P}_1)\mathbf{z}_1 \\ &= [(\mathbf{I}_n - \mathbf{P}_1)\mathbf{z}_0]'(\mathbf{z}_0 - \mathbf{z}_1) + (\mathbf{z}_0 - \mathbf{z}_1)'(\mathbf{I}_n - \mathbf{P}_1)\mathbf{z}_1 \\ &= [\mathbf{P}^{(2)}(\mathbf{I}_n - \mathbf{P}_1)\mathbf{z}_0]'(\mathbf{z}_0 - \mathbf{z}_1) \end{aligned}$$

since $\mathbf{P}^{(2)}(\mathbf{z}_0 - \mathbf{z}_1) = \mathbf{z}_0 - \mathbf{z}_1$ and from (8.3.1)

$$(\mathbf{z}_0 - \mathbf{z}_1)'\mathbf{P}^{(2)}(\mathbf{I}_n - \mathbf{P}_1)\mathbf{z}_1 = 0 .$$

Substituting from (8.3.2) leads to

$$\begin{aligned} b &= (\mathbf{z}_0 - \mathbf{z}_1)'(\mathbf{I}_n - \mathbf{P}_1)\mathbf{P}^{(2)}(\mathbf{z}_0 - \mathbf{z}_1) \\ &= (\mathbf{z}_0 - \mathbf{z}_1)'(\mathbf{I}_n - \mathbf{P}_1)(\mathbf{z}_0 - \mathbf{z}_1) \end{aligned}$$

and the lemma is proved.

An alternative expression for b is given by

$$b = (\mathbf{y}_{m,0} - \mathbf{y}_{m,1})'(\mathbf{I}_m - \mathbf{T}_1)(\mathbf{y}_{m,0} - \mathbf{y}_{m,1}) \qquad (8.3.4)$$

and provided $\mathbf{y}_{m,0}$ and $\mathbf{y}_{m,1}$ are both unique and unequal, $b > 0$ as $\mathbf{I}_m - \mathbf{T}_1$ is positive definite. This form of b is derived in Wilkinson (1958a and b).

8.4 An example (Kruskal, 1960)

Consider a randomised block design with $E[y_{ij}] = \theta_{ij} = \mu + \alpha_i + \beta_j$ for $i = 1, 2, \ldots, I$ and $j = 1, 2, \ldots, J$. From (§6.5) the least squares estimate θ_{ij0} of θ_{ij} is given by

$$\theta_{ij0} = \mu_0 + \alpha_{i0} + \beta_{j0} = \overline{y}_{i.} + \overline{y}_{.j} - \overline{y}_{..}\,.$$

Suppose that the observation y_{IJ} is missing and denote its estimate by u; then, from the above theory, u is also the least squares estimate of θ_{IJ} and equation (8.1.1) becomes

$$u = (y_{I*} + u)/J + (y_{*J} + u)/I - (y_{**} + u)/IJ,$$

where the "star" notation denotes summation on the observed variables; thus $y_{I*} = \sum_{j=1}^{J-1} y_{Ij}$ and $y_{**} = IJ\overline{y}_{..} - y_{IJ}$. We also note that $\boldsymbol{\theta}_0^{(2)} = (0, \ldots, 0, u)'$. Solving the above equation for u gives

$$u = (Iy_{I*} + Jy_{*J} - y_{**})/(I-1)(J-1),$$

and since $E[u] = \mu + \alpha_I + \beta_J = \theta_{IJ}$, u is an unbiased estimate of θ_{IJ}.

Suppose we wish to test the hypothesis H that $\alpha_1 = \alpha_2 = \ldots = \alpha_I = 0$. Then when H is true, the least squares estimate of θ_{ij} is $\overline{y}_{.j}$ and if we denote the new estimate of y_{IJ} under H by v we have by equation (8.2.1) that

$$v = (y_{*J} + v)/I, \qquad (8.4.1)$$

or $v = y_{*J}/(I-1)$.

To obtain the residual s.s. we evaluate

$$\mathbf{z}_0'(\mathbf{I} - \mathbf{P}_0)\mathbf{z}_0 = \sum_i \sum_j (y_{ij} - \overline{y}_{i.} - \overline{y}_{.j} + \overline{y}_{..})^2$$

with y_{IJ} replaced by its estimate u. The numerator s.s. can be calculated in two ways. Firstly we can evaluate $\mathbf{z}_1'(\mathbf{I} - \mathbf{P}_1)\mathbf{z}_1 = \sum_i \sum_j (y_{ij} - \overline{y}_{.j})^2$ with y_{IJ} replaced by v and then obtain the appropriate s.s. by subtraction. Alternatively we can calculate the bias which will be $(u - v)^2(I-1)/I$, since from (8.4.1) $(1 - 1/I)v = y_{*J}/I$ and $\mathbf{T}_1 = 1/I$, giving (cf. equation (8.3.4))

$$b = (u - v)(1 - 1/I)(u - v).$$

Thus the numerator s.s. is now

$$\sum_i \sum_j (\bar{y}_{i.} - \bar{y}_{..})^2 - (u - v)^2 (I - 1)/I$$

where y_{IJ} is replaced by u; the constant term in the F statistic will be $[(I - 1)(J - 1) - 1]/(I - 1)$.

We note that the hypotheses of no-treatment effects and no-block effects are no longer orthogonal since we are not dealing with Ω and ω but with Ω_1 and ω_1. However, as we are concerned mainly with inferences about the treatment effects $\{\alpha_i\}$ the order of nesting is fixed. A table setting out the calculations is given in Kempthorne (1952, p.97).

8.5 An approximate test

An approximate F test (Yates, 1933) is obtained by dropping the negative correction for bias from the numerator, and this implies that we would only have to calculate u which is then used throughout. The F statistic would then be too large, and if the approximation leads to an F value which is not statistically significant, then one can be sure that the correct F value would also be not statistically significant. In some problems this approximation is very good, and in others it is poor; there seems to be no general way of deciding in advance.

8.6 Analysis of covariance method

No discussion on the question of missing observations would be complete without mention of the analysis of covariance technique. The method is to assume that the missing observations are zero and to introduce concomitant variables having a value -1 corresponding to the missing observations, and zero values elsewhere. For example, in our randomised blocks design considered above we assume the model

$$E[y_{ij}] = \theta_{ij} = \mu + \alpha_i + \beta_j + \gamma z_{ij}$$

where $y_{IJ} = 0$ and $z_{ij} = -\delta_{iI}\delta_{jJ}$. To find γ_0, the least squares estimate, we first of all derive the residual $\sum_i \sum_j (y_{ij} - \bar{y}_{i.} - \bar{y}_{.j} + \bar{y}_{..})^2$ with $\gamma = 0$; then, putting $y_{IJ} = 0$ and replacing y_{ij} by $y_{ij} - \gamma z_{ij}$, we minimise this residual with respect to γ (cf. §7.3). We therefore minimise

$$\sum_i \sum_j \{(y_{ij} - \bar{y}_{i.} - \bar{y}_{.j} + \bar{y}_{..}) - \gamma(z_{ij} - \bar{z}_{i.} - \bar{z}_{.j} + \bar{z}_{..})\}^2$$

or $R_{yy} - 2\gamma R_{yz} + \gamma^2 R_{zz}$, say, giving $\gamma_0 = R_{yz}/R_{zz}$. It is readily shown that $R_{yz} = (I y_{I*} + J y_{*J} - y_{**})/IJ$ and $R_{zz} = (I - 1)(J - 1)/IJ$ and hence

$$\begin{aligned}\gamma_0 &= (Iy_{I*} + Jy_{*J} - y_{**})/(I-1)(J-1)\\ &= u\,.\end{aligned}$$

Thus the covariance method leads to the same estimate u of §8.4, and the reason for this is obvious since all we are effectively doing is replacing y_{IJ} by γ and minimising the residual with respect to γ. We note that the residual s.s. for the F test of H has the alternative form

$$R_{yy} - \gamma_0^2 R_{zz} \quad \text{where} \quad y_{IJ} = 0 \text{ in } R_{yy}\,.$$

In conclusion we see that the covariance method will lead to the same F statistic as before. However, the variance of γ_0 for the covariance method will be greater by σ^2 than the variance of u for the previous method, for although y_{IJ} is put equal to zero, it will still have a variance σ^2. For a discussion on this difference cf. Fairfield Smith (1957).

8.7 Application to regression analysis

Suppose that

$$\begin{aligned}E[\mathbf{y}] &= E\begin{bmatrix}\mathbf{y}_{n-m}\\ \\ \mathbf{y}_m\end{bmatrix},\\ &= \begin{bmatrix}\mathbf{X}_{n-m}\\ \\ \mathbf{X}_m\end{bmatrix}\boldsymbol{\beta}\,,\\ &= \mathbf{X}\boldsymbol{\beta}\,,\end{aligned}$$

where $\mathbf{X}$ is an $n \times r$ matrix of rank r and the m observations $\mathbf{y}_m$ are "missing". We can obtain a direct estimate of $\boldsymbol{\beta}$, namely

$$\boldsymbol{\beta}_0 = (\mathbf{X}'_{n-m}\mathbf{X}_{n-m})^{-1}\mathbf{X}_{n-m}\mathbf{y}_{n-m} \tag{8.7.1}$$

using the reduced model $E[\mathbf{y}_{n-m}] = \mathbf{X}_{n-m}\boldsymbol{\beta}$, but in many situations we may want to maintain the symmetry of the original model by simply estimating the missing observations. A good example of this is the fitting of response surfaces with missing observations (Draper, 1961); also we know that any general linear model in experimental design can be written simply as a multiple regression model (cf. Tocher, 1952).

A computational method for estimating the missing observations is given by Tocher, and we now show that it is essentially the analysis of covariance method. The first step is to find the least squares estimate $\mathbf{b}$ of $\boldsymbol{\beta}$ with $\mathbf{y}_m = \mathbf{0}$; thus

$$\mathbf{b} = (\mathbf{X}'\mathbf{X})^{-1}\mathbf{X}'\mathbf{y} ,$$
$$= (\mathbf{X}'\mathbf{X})^{-1}\mathbf{X}'_{n-m}\mathbf{y}_{n-m} . \tag{8.7.2}$$

We next consider the augmented model

$$E[\mathbf{y}] = \mathbf{X}\boldsymbol{\beta} + \mathbf{Z}\boldsymbol{\gamma}$$

where

$$\boldsymbol{\gamma} = (\gamma_1, \gamma_2, \ldots, \gamma_m)',$$

$$-\mathbf{Z} = \begin{bmatrix} \mathbf{0} \\ \mathbf{I}_m \end{bmatrix}$$

and

$$\mathbf{y} = (\mathbf{y}'_{n-m}, \mathbf{0}')'.$$

From equation (7.1.3) we have

$$\gamma_0 = [\mathbf{Z}'(\mathbf{I}_n - \mathbf{P}_0)\mathbf{Z}]^{-1}\mathbf{Z}'(\mathbf{I}_n - \mathbf{P}_0)\mathbf{y}$$

and substituting

$$\mathbf{P}_0 = \mathbf{X}(\mathbf{X}'\mathbf{X})^{-1}\mathbf{X}$$

leads to

$$\gamma_0 = [\mathbf{I}_m - \mathbf{X}_m(\mathbf{X}'\mathbf{X})^{-1}\mathbf{X}'_m]^{-1}\mathbf{X}_m(\mathbf{X}'\mathbf{X})^{-1}\mathbf{X}_{n-m}\mathbf{y}_{n-m} .$$

But

$$\begin{bmatrix} \mathbf{0} \\ \mathbf{y}_{m,0} \end{bmatrix} = -\mathbf{Z}\boldsymbol{\gamma}_0 = \begin{bmatrix} \mathbf{0} \\ \boldsymbol{\gamma}_0 \end{bmatrix}$$

and therefore, from (8.7.2),

$$\mathbf{y}_{m,0} = [\mathbf{I}_m - \mathbf{X}_m(\mathbf{X}'\mathbf{X})^{-1}\mathbf{X}'_m]^{-1}\mathbf{X}_m\mathbf{b} . \tag{8.7.3}$$

Finally

$$\boldsymbol{\beta}_0 = (\mathbf{X}'\mathbf{X})^{-1}\mathbf{X}'\mathbf{z}_0 \tag{8.7.4}$$

where $\mathbf{z}_0 = (\mathbf{y}'_{n-m}, \mathbf{y}'_{m,0})'$ and from our general theory we know that equations (8.7.1) and (8.7.4) are equivalent. Thus to estimate $\boldsymbol{\beta}_0$ we carry out a standard regression analysis with the missing observations given zero values to obtain $\mathbf{b}$; then we evaluate $\mathbf{y}_{m,0}$ from (8.7.3) and perform the standard analysis using this estimate for the missing observations. This is Tocher's method, though his derivation is different.

We note in passing that if $\mathbf{X}$ has rank less than r and identifiability constraints $\mathbf{H}\boldsymbol{\beta} = \mathbf{0}$ are introduced, the only change in the above theory is to replace $(\mathbf{X}'\mathbf{X})$ by $(\mathbf{X}'\mathbf{X} + \mathbf{H}'\mathbf{H})$ in equations (8.7.2) to

(8.7.4). This is most easily seen by deriving (8.7.3) directly from the general theory of §8.1. Recalling equation (8.1.6), namely

$$(\mathbf{I}_m - \mathbf{T}_0)\mathbf{y}_{m,0} = \mathbf{S}_0\mathbf{y}_{n-m},$$

we have

$$\mathbf{T}_0 = \mathbf{X}_m(\mathbf{X}'\mathbf{X})^{-1}\mathbf{X}'_m,$$

and

$$\mathbf{S}_0 = \mathbf{X}_{n-m}(\mathbf{X}'\mathbf{X})^{-1}\mathbf{X}'_m$$

leading immediately to (8.7.3). Introducing identifiability constraints only changes $\mathbf{P}_0$ to $\mathbf{X}(\mathbf{X}'\mathbf{X}+\mathbf{H}'\mathbf{H})^{-1}\mathbf{X}'$.

The relative merits of these two slightly different approaches, together with examples, are discussed in Draper (1961) and Wilkinson (1960).

EXERCISE 12. By considering the variance matrix of $\boldsymbol{\beta}_0$ prove that $(\mathbf{X}'_{n-m}\mathbf{X}_{n-m})^{-1} = (\mathbf{X}'\mathbf{X})^{-1} + (\mathbf{X}'\mathbf{X})^{-1}\mathbf{X}'_m[\mathbf{I}_m - \mathbf{X}_m(\mathbf{X}'\mathbf{X})^{-1}\mathbf{X}'_m]^{-1}\mathbf{X}_m(\mathbf{X}'\mathbf{X})^{-1}$.

EXERCISE 13. Show that

$$\|(\mathbf{y}_{n-m} - \mathbf{X}_{m-n}\boldsymbol{\beta}_0)\| = \|(\mathbf{z}_0 - \mathbf{X}\boldsymbol{\beta}_0\|.$$

8.8 Additional references and related topics

Missing observations in analysis of covariance models: Wilkinson (1957).

The analysis of covariance as a missing plot technique: Coons (1957).

Analysis of variance of a randomised block design with missing observations: Glenn and Kramer (1958).

General references on missing observations in experimental designs are Biggers (1959, 1961), Cochran and Cox (1957), Davies (1956), and Kempthorne (1952). A related topic is that of missing observations in the *independent* variable x, or, more generally, dealing with incomplete multivariate data as a whole. References relevant to this subject are given in Glasser (1964) and Trawinski and Bargmann (1964).

The problem of mixed-up observations is considered in Tocher (1952) and Biggers (1959, 1961).

An allied problem to that of missing observations is the question of extra or duplicate observations. This is considered by Plackett (1950) and Tocher (1952) from the regression point of view, and by Kruskal (1960) using the vector space, coordinate-free approach which we have used throughout this monograph.

A final problem is that of dealing with dubious observations or outliers, and the reader is referred to Ferguson (1960), Bross (1961), Quesenberry and David (1961), and Thompson and Willke (1963).

CHAPTER 9

MULTIVARIATE LINEAR HYPOTHESES

9.1 Introduction

Much of the basic theory of the univariate linear hypothesis given in the first few chapters extends naturally to the multivariate case, though of course the distribution theory is more difficult. In this chapter we shall define what we mean by a multivariate linear hypothesis and indicate briefly how some of the univariate results can be extended.

Suppose we are given n independent multivariate normal vectors $\mathbf{y}_i = (y_{i1}, y_{i2}, \ldots, y_{it})'$ with means $\boldsymbol{\theta}_i = (\theta_{i1}, \theta_{i2}, \ldots, \theta_{it})'$ and a common $t \times t$ dispersion matrix $\boldsymbol{\Sigma} = [(\sigma_{ij})]$; thus $\mathbf{y}_i = \boldsymbol{\theta}_i + \mathbf{u}_i$ where $\mathbf{u}_i$ is $\mathcal{N}[\mathbf{0}, \boldsymbol{\Sigma}]$. Let

$$\mathbf{Y}' = [(y_{ij})]' = (\mathbf{y}_1, \mathbf{y}_2, \ldots, \mathbf{y}_n)$$

with $\boldsymbol{\Theta}'$ and $\mathbf{U}'$ defined in a similar manner giving

$$\mathbf{Y} = \boldsymbol{\Theta} + \mathbf{U}. \tag{9.1.1}$$

As in the univariate case, a multivariate linear hypothesis is defined in terms of two vector spaces Ω and ω having dimensions p and $p-q$ respectively. We make the assumption G that the columns of $\boldsymbol{\Theta}$ all lie in Ω; the hypothesis H specifies that they all lie in ω.

We can split up the above multivariate model into t univariate models as follows. Let $\mathbf{y}^{(i)} = (y_{1i}, y_{2i}, \ldots, y_{ni})'$ be the ith column of $\mathbf{Y}$; $\boldsymbol{\theta}^{(i)}$ and $\mathbf{u}^{(i)}$ are similarly defined. Then from (9.1.1) $\mathbf{y}^{(i)} = \boldsymbol{\theta}^{(i)} + \mathbf{u}^{(i)}$ where $\mathbf{u}^{(i)}$ is $\mathcal{N}[\mathbf{0}, \sigma_{ii}\mathbf{I}_n]$, $G : \boldsymbol{\theta}^{(i)} \in \Omega$ and $H : \boldsymbol{\theta}^{(i)} \in \omega$ for $i = 1, 2, \ldots, t$. Although these t univariate models are not independent as $\operatorname{cov}(\mathbf{y}^{(i)}, \mathbf{y}^{(j)}) = \sigma_{ij}\mathbf{I}_n$, we shall now show that we can treat them as independent models as far as maximum likelihood estimation is concerned.

Let $\boldsymbol{\Theta}_0$, $\boldsymbol{\Sigma}_0$, $\boldsymbol{\Theta}_1$ and $\boldsymbol{\Sigma}_1$ be the maximum likelihood estimates of $\boldsymbol{\Theta}$ and $\boldsymbol{\Sigma}$ under G and H respectively. Then the likelihood function $L[\boldsymbol{\Theta}]$ for $\mathbf{y}_1, \mathbf{y}_2, \ldots, \mathbf{y}_n$ is given by

$$L[\boldsymbol{\Theta}] = (2\pi)^{-nt/2}|\boldsymbol{\Sigma}|^{-n/2}\exp\{-\tfrac{1}{2}\sum_{r=1}^{n}(\mathbf{y}_r - \boldsymbol{\theta}_r)'\boldsymbol{\Sigma}^{-1}(\mathbf{y}_r - \boldsymbol{\theta}_r)\}.$$

If $\boldsymbol{\Sigma}^{-1} = [(\sigma^{ij})]$ then

$$\sum_{r=1}^{n} (\mathbf{y}_r - \boldsymbol{\theta}_r)'\boldsymbol{\Sigma}^{-1}(\mathbf{y}_r - \boldsymbol{\theta}_r) = \sum_r \sum_i \sum_j u_{ri}\,\sigma^{ij} u_{rj}$$

$$= \sum_i \sum_j (\mathbf{U}'\mathbf{U})_{ij}\,\sigma^{ji}$$

$$= \sum_i (\mathbf{U}'\mathbf{U}\boldsymbol{\Sigma}^{-1})_{ii}$$

$$= \mathrm{tr}\,[\mathbf{U}'\mathbf{U}\boldsymbol{\Sigma}^{-1}]$$

$$= \mathrm{tr}[(\mathbf{Y}-\boldsymbol{\Theta})'(\mathbf{Y}-\boldsymbol{\Theta})\boldsymbol{\Sigma}^{-1}].$$

To find the maximum likelihood estimates $\boldsymbol{\Sigma}_0$ and $\boldsymbol{\Theta}_0$ we maximise $\log L[\boldsymbol{\Theta}] = \text{constant} - \frac{n}{2}\log|\boldsymbol{\Sigma}| - \frac{1}{2}\mathrm{tr}[(\mathbf{Y}-\boldsymbol{\Theta})'(\mathbf{Y}-\boldsymbol{\Theta})\boldsymbol{\Sigma}^{-1}]$ subject to $\mathbf{P}_0\boldsymbol{\Theta} = \boldsymbol{\Theta}$. Introducing a symmetric matrix of Lagrange multipliers $\boldsymbol{\Phi}$, we have to differentiate

$$-\frac{n}{2}\log|\boldsymbol{\Sigma}| - \frac{1}{2}\mathrm{tr}[(\mathbf{Y}-\boldsymbol{\Theta})'(\mathbf{Y}-\boldsymbol{\Theta})\boldsymbol{\Sigma}^{-1}] + \mathrm{tr}[(\mathbf{I}-\mathbf{P}_0)\boldsymbol{\Theta}\boldsymbol{\Phi}] \qquad (9.1.2)$$

with respect to the elements of $\boldsymbol{\Sigma}^{-1}$ and $\boldsymbol{\Theta}$. Using the results of Appendix II, the maximum likelihood equations are

$$\mathbf{Y}\boldsymbol{\Sigma}^{-1} - \boldsymbol{\Theta}\boldsymbol{\Sigma}^{-1} + (\mathbf{I}-\mathbf{P}_0)\boldsymbol{\Phi} = \mathbf{0} \qquad (9.1.3)$$

$$\frac{n}{2}\boldsymbol{\Sigma} - \frac{1}{2}(\mathbf{Y}-\boldsymbol{\Theta})'(\mathbf{Y}-\boldsymbol{\Theta}) = \mathbf{0}$$

and

$$(\mathbf{I}-\mathbf{P}_0)\boldsymbol{\Theta} = \mathbf{0}.$$

Premultiplying (9.1.3) by $\mathbf{P}_0$ gives $\boldsymbol{\Theta}_0 = \mathbf{P}_0\mathbf{Y}$ and hence $\boldsymbol{\Sigma}_0 = \mathbf{Y}'(\mathbf{I}-\mathbf{P}_0)\mathbf{Y}/n$. Thus

$$\boldsymbol{\theta}_0^{(i)} = \mathbf{P}_0\mathbf{y}^{(i)} \quad \text{and} \quad (\sigma_{ii})_0 = \mathbf{y}^{(i)\prime}(\mathbf{I}-\mathbf{P}_0)\mathbf{y}^{(i)}/n$$

which are the maximum likelihood estimates for the univariate model $\mathbf{y}^{(i)} = \boldsymbol{\theta}^{(i)} + \mathbf{u}^{(i)}$.

9.2 Test statistics

The likelihood ratio test statistic for testing H is

$$L[H\,|\,G] = |\boldsymbol{\Sigma}_0|^{n/2} / |\boldsymbol{\Sigma}_1|^{n/2}$$

and the test statistic used is

$$U = \frac{|\boldsymbol{\Sigma}_0|}{|\boldsymbol{\Sigma}_1|} = \frac{|\mathbf{Y}'(\mathbf{I}-\mathbf{P}_0)\mathbf{Y}|}{|\mathbf{Y}'(\mathbf{I}-\mathbf{P}_1)\mathbf{Y}|},$$

a monotonic function of the likelihood ratio. To find the distribution of U we use a multivariate analogue of Cochran's theorem which we now state (cf. Anderson (1958) and Hogg (1963)).

Theorem 9.2.1. Let $\mathbf{x}_1, \mathbf{x}_2, \ldots, \mathbf{x}_n$ be random variables which are identically and independently distributed as $\mathcal{N}[\mathbf{0}, \mathbf{I}_t]$ and let $\mathbf{A}_1, \mathbf{A}_2, \ldots, \mathbf{A}_m$ be a sequence of $n \times n$ matrices with ranks $r_1, r_2, \ldots, r_m$ such that $\sum_i \mathbf{A}_i = \mathbf{I}_n$. Then if one (and therefore all) of the conditions of lemma 4.2.1 hold, the generalised quadratic expressions $\sum_r \sum_s a^i_{rs} \mathbf{x}_r \mathbf{x}'_s$, where $[(a^i_{rs})] = \mathbf{A}_i$, are independently distributed as $W[\mathbf{I}_t; r_i]$, the Wishart distribution with r_i degrees of freedom.

Proof. The method of proof is exactly the same as for the univariate case. One makes an orthogonal transformation $\mathbf{z}^{(i)} = \mathbf{T}'\mathbf{x}^{(i)}$, where $\mathbf{T}$ is the orthogonal matrix defined in the proof of theorem 4.2.2, giving

$$\begin{aligned} \sum_r \sum_s a^1_{rs} \mathbf{x}_r \mathbf{x}'_s &= \mathbf{X}'\mathbf{A}_1\mathbf{X} \\ &= \mathbf{Z}'\mathbf{T}'\mathbf{A}_1\mathbf{T}\mathbf{Z} \\ &= \sum_{r=1}^{r_1} \mathbf{z}_r \mathbf{z}'_r . \end{aligned}$$

Similarly
$$\mathbf{X}'\mathbf{A}_2\mathbf{X} = \sum_{r=r_1+1}^{r_1+r_2} \mathbf{z}_r \mathbf{z}'_r \quad \text{etc.}$$

Now the dispersion matrix of $\mathbf{z}_r$ is $\mathbf{T}'\mathbf{I}\mathbf{T} = \mathbf{I}_t$ and therefore $\mathbf{z}_1, \ldots, \mathbf{z}_n$ are identically and independently distributed as $\mathcal{N}[\mathbf{0}, \mathbf{I}_t]$ Thus the forms $\mathbf{X}'\mathbf{A}_i\mathbf{X}$ are independently distributed as $W[\mathbf{I}_t; r_i]$: a full discussion on the derivation and properties of the Wishart distribution is given in Anderson (1958, Chapter 7).

Corollary. If the $\mathbf{x}_i$ are $\mathcal{N}[\mathbf{0}, \boldsymbol{\Sigma}]$ then the only modification in the theorem is that the forms $\mathbf{X}'\mathbf{A}_i\mathbf{X}$ are now distributed independently as $W[\boldsymbol{\Sigma}; r_i]$. To prove this one simply makes the transformation $\mathbf{y}_i = \mathbf{V}^{-1}\mathbf{x}_i$ where $\mathbf{V}\mathbf{V}' = \boldsymbol{\Sigma}$, for then $\mathbf{y}_i$ is $\mathcal{N}[\mathbf{0}, \mathbf{I}_t]$. The non-singular matrix $\mathbf{V}$ exists since $\boldsymbol{\Sigma}$ is positive definite (Appendix I, lemma 1). The case when $\boldsymbol{\Sigma}$ is singular is also discussed in Anderson (1958).

EXERCISE 14. Prove that the multivariate linear model can be transformed by a suitable orthogonal transformation to the following canonical form: the vectors $\mathbf{z}_i$ are $\mathcal{N}[\boldsymbol{\phi}_i, \boldsymbol{\Sigma}]$ for $i = 1, 2, \ldots, n$,

$$G : \boldsymbol{\phi}_{p+1} = \ldots = \boldsymbol{\phi}_n = \mathbf{0}$$

$$H : \boldsymbol{\phi}_1 = \ldots = \boldsymbol{\phi}_q = \boldsymbol{\phi}_{p+1} = \ldots = \boldsymbol{\phi}_n = \mathbf{0}$$

$$U = \frac{\left| \sum_{r=p+1}^{n} \mathbf{z}_r \mathbf{z}_r' \right|}{\left| \sum_{r=1}^{q} \mathbf{z}_r \mathbf{z}_r' + \sum_{r=p+1}^{n} \mathbf{z}_r \mathbf{z}_r' \right|} . \qquad \text{(Hsu, 1941b)}$$

We now apply the above corollary to the test statistic U. When H is true,

$$U = \frac{|n \boldsymbol{\Sigma}_0|}{|n \boldsymbol{\Sigma}_0 + n(\boldsymbol{\Sigma}_1 - \boldsymbol{\Sigma}_0)|}, \quad = \frac{|\mathbf{B}|}{|\mathbf{B} + \mathbf{A}|}, \text{ say,}$$

where $\mathbf{B} = (\mathbf{Y} - \boldsymbol{\Theta})'(\mathbf{I} - \mathbf{P}_0)(\mathbf{Y} - \boldsymbol{\Theta})$ and

$$\mathbf{A} = (\mathbf{Y} - \boldsymbol{\Theta})'(\mathbf{P}_0 - \mathbf{P}_1)(\mathbf{Y} - \boldsymbol{\Theta}).$$

Since $\mathbf{I} = (\mathbf{I} - \mathbf{P}_0) + (\mathbf{P}_0 - \mathbf{P}_1) + \mathbf{P}_1$ is a decomposition into idempotent matrices, theorem 9.2.1 applies, and $\mathbf{A}$ and $\mathbf{B}$ are independently distributed as $W[\boldsymbol{\Sigma}; n-p]$ and $W[\boldsymbol{\Sigma}; q]$ respectively when H is true. From this the distribution of U can be found (Anderson, 1958, Chapter 8) and is denoted by $U_{t,q,n-p}$ when H is true; for some values of t this distribution has a simple expression, but in general it is very complicated.

Several other test criteria for testing H have been put forward and they are based on the so-called "invariance principle" (cf. §5.1). Using the canonical form of exercise 14, we see that the multivariate linear hypothesis is invariant under the following class of transformations $\mathcal{T}$:

(i) $\mathbf{z}_i^* = \mathbf{z}_i + \boldsymbol{\delta}_i$ for $i = q+1, \ldots, p$ and arbitrary $\boldsymbol{\delta}_i$,

(ii) $(\mathbf{z}_1^*, \ldots, \mathbf{z}_q^*) = (\mathbf{z}_1, \ldots, \mathbf{z}_q)\mathbf{T}_1$,
$(\mathbf{z}_{p+1}^*, \ldots, \mathbf{z}_n^*) = (\mathbf{z}_{p+1}, \ldots, \mathbf{z}_n)\mathbf{T}_2$ for arbitrary orthogonal matrices $\mathbf{T}_1$ and $\mathbf{T}_2$, and

(iii) $\mathbf{z}_i^* = \mathbf{R}\mathbf{z}_i$ $(i = 1, 2, \ldots, q, p+1, \ldots, n)$ for any non-singular matrix $\mathbf{R}$. When $t > 1$ and $q > 1$ there does not exist a U.M.P. test among the class of tests invariant under $\mathcal{T}$ (Lehmann, 1958, §7.10) and so various invariant tests have been suggested. All these tests which we now list from Ito (1962) are functions of the roots of $|\mathbf{A} - \lambda\mathbf{B}| = 0$; these roots being invariant under $\mathcal{T}$ (Anderson, 1958, Chapter 8).

(1) Wilks's criterion (Wilks, 1932 and Hsu, 1940)

$$= |\mathbf{A}| / |\mathbf{A} + \mathbf{B}|.$$

(2) Likelihood ratio statistic (Wilks, 1932 and Hsu, 1940)

$$U = |\mathbf{B}|/|\mathbf{B}+\mathbf{A}|.$$

(3) Lawley's V and Hotelling's T_0^2 (Lawley, 1938 and Hotelling, 1951)

$$V = \mathrm{tr}[\mathbf{A}\mathbf{B}^{-1}] = T_0^2/(n-p).$$

(4) Roy's largest root, $\lambda_{\max}$ say (Roy, 1957).

(5) The smallest root $\lambda_{\min}$ (Anderson, 1958).

(6) The statistic $\mathrm{tr}[\mathbf{A}(\mathbf{A}+\mathbf{B})^{-1}]$ (Anderson, 1958).

(7) Three other test criteria are given by Pillai (1955).

As all these statistics are functions of the roots of $|\mathbf{A}-\lambda\mathbf{B}| = 0$ one would, in theory, be able to derive their distributions if the joint distribution of the roots was known. When H is true, the distribution of the roots is given in Anderson (1958, Chapter 13). However, all the above statistics have complicated distributions even in the null case when H is true, and so, when n is big enough, large sample chi-squared approximations are used—cf. Anderson (1958, §8.6 and §8.10).

9.3 Examples

The first example we consider is that of multivariate regression. Suppose that $\Omega = \{\boldsymbol{\theta}^{(i)} : \boldsymbol{\theta}^{(i)} = \mathbf{X}\boldsymbol{\beta}_i\}$ where $\mathbf{X}$ is an $n \times p$ matrix of rank p; then $G : \boldsymbol{\Theta} = \mathbf{X}\mathbf{B}$ where $\mathbf{B} = (\boldsymbol{\beta}_1, \ldots, \boldsymbol{\beta}_t)$. We wish to test the hypothesis H that $\mathbf{F}\mathbf{B} = \mathbf{0}$ where $\mathbf{F}$ is a $q \times p$ matrix of rank q. Now $\mathbf{F}\boldsymbol{\beta}_i = \mathbf{F}(\mathbf{X}'\mathbf{X})^{-1}\mathbf{X}'\boldsymbol{\theta}^{(i)} = \mathbf{0}$ and thus $\Omega = R[\mathbf{X}]$ and $\omega = \Omega \cap N[\mathbf{F}(\mathbf{X}'\mathbf{X})^{-1}\mathbf{X}']$. Hence from our univariate theory (lemmas 4.4.2 and 4.4.3)

$$\mathbf{P}_0 = \mathbf{X}(\mathbf{X}'\mathbf{X})^{-1}\mathbf{X}'$$

$$\mathbf{P}_0 - \mathbf{P}_1 = \mathbf{X}(\mathbf{X}'\mathbf{X})^{-1}\mathbf{F}'[\mathbf{F}(\mathbf{X}'\mathbf{X})^{-1}\mathbf{F}']^{-1}\mathbf{F}(\mathbf{X}'\mathbf{X})^{-1}\mathbf{X}'$$

and our test statistic U is readily calculated. These results are derived by Kabe (1963) using a different approach.

If $\mathbf{B} = (\mathbf{B}_1', \mathbf{B}_2')'$ then a special case of H above is the hypothesis that $\mathbf{B}_1 = \mathbf{0}$ where $\mathbf{B}_1$ is a $q \times t$ matrix. Here $\mathbf{F} = (\mathbf{I}_q, \mathbf{0})$ and $\mathbf{B}_{1,0}$, the maximum likelihood estimate of $\mathbf{B}_1$, is given by

$$\begin{aligned}\mathbf{B}_{1,0} &= \mathbf{F}\mathbf{B}_0 \quad \text{(by theorem 3.5.1)}\\ &= \mathbf{F}(\mathbf{X}'\mathbf{X})^{-1}\mathbf{X}'\boldsymbol{\Theta}_0\\ &= \mathbf{F}(\mathbf{X}'\mathbf{X})^{-1}\mathbf{X}'\mathbf{Y}.\end{aligned}$$

If we partition $\mathbf{X}$ in the form $(\mathbf{X}_1, \mathbf{X}_2)$, where $\mathbf{X}_1$ consists of the first q columns, then

$$\mathbf{X}'\mathbf{X} = \begin{bmatrix} \mathbf{X}_1'\mathbf{X}_1, & \mathbf{X}_1'\mathbf{X}_2 \\ \mathbf{X}_2'\mathbf{X}_1, & \mathbf{X}_2'\mathbf{X}_2 \end{bmatrix}$$

$$= \begin{bmatrix} \mathbf{X}_{11}, & \mathbf{X}_{12} \\ \mathbf{X}_{21}, & \mathbf{X}_{22} \end{bmatrix}, \text{ say.}$$

Now

$$(\mathbf{X}'\mathbf{X})^{-1} = \begin{bmatrix} (\mathbf{X}_{11} - \mathbf{X}_{12}\mathbf{X}_{22}^{-1}\mathbf{X}_{21})^{-1}, & (\mathbf{X}_{12}\mathbf{X}_{22}^{-1}\mathbf{X}_{21} - \mathbf{X}_{11})^{-1}\mathbf{X}_{12}\mathbf{X}_{22}^{-1} \\ (\mathbf{X}_{21}\mathbf{X}_{11}^{-1}\mathbf{X}_{12} - \mathbf{X}_{22})^{-1}\mathbf{X}_{21}\mathbf{X}_{11}^{-1}, & (\mathbf{X}_{22} - \mathbf{X}_{21}\mathbf{X}_{11}^{-1}\mathbf{X}_{12})^{-1} \end{bmatrix} \tag{9.3.1}$$

(by Aitken (1954), p. 139) and therefore

$$[\mathbf{F}(\mathbf{X}'\mathbf{X})^{-1}\mathbf{F}']^{-1} = \mathbf{X}_{11} - \mathbf{X}_{12}\mathbf{X}_{22}^{-1}\mathbf{X}_{21} = \mathbf{X}_{11.2}, \text{ say},$$

giving

$$\mathbf{Y}'(\mathbf{P}_0 - \mathbf{P}_1)\mathbf{Y} = \mathbf{B}_{1,0}'\mathbf{X}_{11.2}\mathbf{B}_{1,0}.$$

Our second example is a multivariate generalisation of the randomised block design where all the observations and unknown parameters are now t-dimensional vectors. Thus $\mathbf{y}_{ij} = \boldsymbol{\mu} + \boldsymbol{\alpha}_i + \boldsymbol{\beta}_j + \mathbf{e}_{ij}$ (for $i = 1, 2, \ldots, I$; $j = 1, 2, \ldots, J$) where the $\mathbf{e}_{ij}$ are independently and identically distributed as $\mathcal{N}[\mathbf{0}, \boldsymbol{\Sigma}]$ and $\sum_i \boldsymbol{\alpha}_i = \sum_j \boldsymbol{\beta}_j = \mathbf{0}$ are the identifiability conditions. As in the univariate case, the model can be written in the form of a regression model $E[\mathbf{Y}] = \mathbf{X}\mathbf{B}$ where $\mathbf{Y}' = (\mathbf{y}_{11}, \mathbf{y}_{12}, \ldots, \mathbf{y}_{IJ})$ and $\mathbf{B}' = (\boldsymbol{\mu}, \boldsymbol{\alpha}_1, \ldots, \boldsymbol{\alpha}_I, \boldsymbol{\beta}_1, \ldots, \boldsymbol{\beta}_J)$. We have shown (§9.1) that a multivariate regression model can be considered as t separate univariate regressions, and therefore the constraints $\Sigma\boldsymbol{\alpha}_i = \Sigma\boldsymbol{\beta}_j = \mathbf{0}$ are suitable as identifiability conditions.

To test the hypothesis $H: \boldsymbol{\alpha}_1 = \ldots = \boldsymbol{\alpha}_I = \mathbf{0}$ we look first of all at the univariate case; here (Table 6.5.2)

$$\mathbf{y}'(\mathbf{P}_0 - \mathbf{P}_1)\mathbf{y} = J\sum_i (y_{i.} - \bar{y}_{..})^2$$

and

$$\mathbf{y}'(\mathbf{I} - \mathbf{P}_0)\mathbf{y} = \sum_i\sum_j (y_{ij} - \bar{y}_{i.} - \bar{y}_{.j} + \bar{y}_{..})^2.$$

As $\mathbf{Y}'\mathbf{A}\mathbf{Y} = \sum_r\sum_s a_{rs}\mathbf{y}_r\mathbf{y}_s'$ we have by analogy

$$\mathbf{Y}'(\mathbf{P}_0 - \mathbf{P}_1)\mathbf{Y} = J\sum_i (\bar{\mathbf{y}}_{i.} - \bar{\mathbf{y}}_{..})(\bar{\mathbf{y}}_{i.} - \bar{\mathbf{y}}_{..})' \quad \text{and}$$

$$\mathbf{Y}'(\mathbf{I} - \mathbf{P}_0)\mathbf{Y} = \sum_i\sum_j (\mathbf{y}_{ij} - \bar{\mathbf{y}}_{i.} - \bar{\mathbf{y}}_{.j} + \bar{\mathbf{y}}_{..})(\mathbf{y}_{ij} - \bar{\mathbf{y}}_{i.} - \bar{\mathbf{y}}_{.j} + \bar{\mathbf{y}}_{..})'.$$

A third class of problems are those associated with testing linear hypotheses about the mean of a multivariate normal distribution. In this case each $\mathbf{y}_i$ is $\mathcal{N}[\boldsymbol{\theta}, \boldsymbol{\Sigma}]$ and G is the assumption that $\boldsymbol{\theta}^{(i)} = \theta_i \mathbf{1}_n$ for $i = 1, 2, \ldots, t$, where θ_i is the ith element of $\boldsymbol{\theta}$. To find the maximum likelihood estimate $\boldsymbol{\theta}_0$ we need only find the estimate θ_{i0} for each of the t univariate models. Thus from example 4 (§3.4), $\theta_{i0} = \mathbf{y}^{(i)\prime}\mathbf{1}_n/n$ and therefore

$$\boldsymbol{\theta}_0 = \mathbf{Y}'\mathbf{1}_n/n = \sum_i \mathbf{y}_i/n = \overline{\mathbf{y}}_.$$

Also

$$\begin{aligned}\boldsymbol{\Sigma}_0 &= \sum_i (\mathbf{y}_i - \boldsymbol{\theta}_0)(\mathbf{y}_i - \boldsymbol{\theta}_0)'/n \\ &= \sum_i (\mathbf{y}_i - \overline{\mathbf{y}}_.)(\mathbf{y}_i - \overline{\mathbf{y}}_.)'/n\end{aligned}$$

and the unbiased estimate of $\boldsymbol{\Sigma}$ is $\mathbf{S} = n\boldsymbol{\Sigma}_0/(n-1)$.

When we come to test the hypothesis H that $\mathbf{A}\boldsymbol{\theta} = \mathbf{0}$, where the rows of $\mathbf{A}$ are linearly independent, we find that according to our general definition, H is not a multivariate linear hypothesis and therefore the above general theory does not apply. In fact H is essentially a univariate hypothesis, and we can therefore obtain a test statistic by applying the Wald principle as follows (cf. §4.4). Since

$$\begin{aligned}D[\mathbf{A}\boldsymbol{\theta}_0] &= D[\mathbf{A}\overline{\mathbf{y}}_.] \\ &= \mathbf{A}\boldsymbol{\Sigma}\mathbf{A}'/n,\end{aligned}$$

we replace $\boldsymbol{\Sigma}$ by its unbiased estimate $\mathbf{S}$ and consider the statistic

$$T^2 = n(\mathbf{A}\boldsymbol{\theta}_0)'(\mathbf{A}\mathbf{S}\mathbf{A}')^{-1}\mathbf{A}\boldsymbol{\theta}_0.$$

This statistic is due to Hotelling (1931) and we now show that it can also be derived using the likelihood ratio principle. We first of all derive the maximum likelihood estimates $\boldsymbol{\theta}_1$ and $\boldsymbol{\Sigma}_1$ under H by maximising (cf. 9.1.2)

$$-\frac{n}{2}\log|\boldsymbol{\Sigma}| - \frac{1}{2}\operatorname{tr}[\sum_r (\mathbf{y}_r - \boldsymbol{\theta})(\mathbf{y}_r - \boldsymbol{\theta})'\boldsymbol{\Sigma}^{-1}] + \operatorname{tr}[\mathbf{A}\boldsymbol{\theta}\boldsymbol{\mu}']$$

with respect to $\boldsymbol{\theta}$ and $\boldsymbol{\Sigma}^{-1}$, where $\boldsymbol{\mu}$ is the Lagrange multiplier. Using Appendix 2, it is readily shown that

$$\boldsymbol{\theta}_1 = (\mathbf{I} - \boldsymbol{\Sigma}_1^{-1}\mathbf{A}(\mathbf{A}'\boldsymbol{\Sigma}_1^{-1}\mathbf{A})\mathbf{A}')\overline{\mathbf{y}}_.$$

and

$$\begin{aligned}n\boldsymbol{\Sigma}_1 &= \sum_i (\mathbf{y}_i - \boldsymbol{\theta}_1)(\mathbf{y}_i - \boldsymbol{\theta}_1)' \\ &= \Sigma(\mathbf{y}_i - \overline{\mathbf{y}}_.)(\mathbf{y}_i - \overline{\mathbf{y}}_.)' + n(\overline{\mathbf{y}}_. - \boldsymbol{\theta}_1)(\overline{\mathbf{y}}_. - \boldsymbol{\theta}_1)'\end{aligned}$$

leading to

$$n\mathbf{A}\boldsymbol{\Sigma}_1\mathbf{A}' = n\mathbf{A}\boldsymbol{\Sigma}_0\mathbf{A}' + n\mathbf{A}\overline{\mathbf{y}}_.\overline{\mathbf{y}}_.'\mathbf{A}'.$$

Instead of considering the likelihood ratio statistic

$$L[H \mid G]^{2/n} = |n\,\boldsymbol{\Sigma}_0| / |n\,\boldsymbol{\Sigma}_1|,$$

we calculate

$$\begin{aligned} l &= |n\mathbf{A}\boldsymbol{\Sigma}_0\mathbf{A}'| / |n\mathbf{A}\boldsymbol{\Sigma}_1\mathbf{A}'| \\ &= |(n-1)\mathbf{A}\mathbf{S}\mathbf{A}'| / |(n-1)\mathbf{A}\mathbf{S}\mathbf{A}' + n\mathbf{A}\bar{\mathbf{y}}_.\bar{\mathbf{y}}_.'\mathbf{A}'|. \end{aligned}$$

At this point we require the following result. For $|\mathbf{B}| \neq 0$

$$\begin{aligned} \begin{vmatrix} \mathbf{B}, & \mathbf{C} \\ \mathbf{D}, & \mathbf{E} \end{vmatrix} &= \begin{vmatrix} \mathbf{B}, & \mathbf{C} \\ \mathbf{D}, & \mathbf{E} \end{vmatrix} \begin{vmatrix} \mathbf{I}, & -\mathbf{B}^{-1}\mathbf{C} \\ \mathbf{0}, & \mathbf{I} \end{vmatrix} \\ &= \begin{vmatrix} \mathbf{B}, & \mathbf{0} \\ \mathbf{D}, & \mathbf{E} - \mathbf{D}\mathbf{B}^{-1}\mathbf{C} \end{vmatrix} \\ &= |\mathbf{B}| . |\mathbf{E} - \mathbf{D}\mathbf{B}^{-1}\mathbf{C}| \end{aligned}$$

and applying this twice gives

$$\begin{aligned} l &= \begin{vmatrix} 1, & n^{1/2}\bar{\mathbf{y}}_.'\mathbf{A}' \\ -n^{1/2}\mathbf{A}\bar{\mathbf{y}}_., & (n-1)\mathbf{A}\mathbf{S}\mathbf{A}' \end{vmatrix}^{-1} |(n-1)\mathbf{A}\mathbf{S}\mathbf{A}'| \\ &= \{1 + n\bar{\mathbf{y}}_.'\mathbf{A}'(\mathbf{A}\mathbf{S}\mathbf{A}')^{-1}\mathbf{A}\bar{\mathbf{y}}_. / (n-1)\}^{-1} \\ &= \{1 + T^2/(n-1)\}^{-1}. \end{aligned}$$

Thus T^2 is a monotonic function of l. If we put $\mathbf{z}_i = \mathbf{A}\mathbf{y}_i$ then $\mathbf{z}_i$ is $\mathcal{N}[\boldsymbol{\phi}, \boldsymbol{\Sigma}^*]$, where $\boldsymbol{\phi} = \mathbf{A}\boldsymbol{\theta}$ and $\boldsymbol{\Sigma}^* = \mathbf{A}\boldsymbol{\Sigma}\mathbf{A}'$; H is now the hypothesis that $\boldsymbol{\phi} = \mathbf{0}$. It can be shown that

$$\begin{aligned} n\boldsymbol{\Sigma}_0^* &= (n-1)\mathbf{S}^* = (n-1)\mathbf{A}\mathbf{S}\mathbf{A}, \\ n(\boldsymbol{\Sigma}_1^* - \boldsymbol{\Sigma}_0^*) &= n\,\bar{\mathbf{z}}_.\bar{\mathbf{z}}_.' = n\mathbf{A}\bar{\mathbf{y}}_.\bar{\mathbf{y}}_.'\mathbf{A}', \end{aligned}$$

and $l^{n/2}$ is the likelihood ratio for testing H under the transformed model. We could have used this approach right at the beginning, but then we would not have obtained our estimate $\boldsymbol{\theta}_1$ under H.

Thus T^2, which can also be written in the form $n\bar{\mathbf{z}}_.'(\mathbf{S}^*)^{-1}\bar{\mathbf{z}}_.$, is based on the likelihood ratio criterion. It is shown in Anderson (1958, corollary 5.2.1) that $[(n-r)/r]\,T^2/(n-1)$, where $r = \text{rank}[\mathbf{A}]$, has a non-central F distribution with r and $n-r$ degrees of freedom respectively and non-centrality parameter $n(\mathbf{A}\boldsymbol{\theta})'(\mathbf{A}\boldsymbol{\Sigma}\mathbf{A}')^{-1}(\mathbf{A}\boldsymbol{\theta})$.

For further examples of testing linear hypotheses about the mean of a multivariate normal, cf. Anderson (1958, Chapter 5) and Rao (1959).

9.4 Testing several hypotheses

When the U statistic is used for testing a sequence of hypotheses $H_1, H_2, \ldots, H_K$ against G, the nested method of §6.1 can still be used, as the product property of the likelihood ratios still holds. However, the separate test procedure may be useless for multivariate hypotheses as no simple relationship exists among the likelihood-ratio test statistics, even when there is orthogonality. This means that even if all the separate tests of H_i against G are not significant we have no confidence that $H_1 \wedge H_2 \wedge \ldots \wedge H_K$ is also acceptable. For this reason we consider alternative test statistics to U and see which one has a simple relationship between the test of $H_1 \wedge \ldots \wedge H_K$ against G and the separate tests of H_i against G.

Suppose that ω_1 and ω_2 are two orthogonal hypotheses, i.e. $\omega_1^p \perp \omega_2^p$, and let $\mathbf{A}_i = \mathbf{Y}'(\mathbf{P}_0 - \mathbf{P}_i)\mathbf{Y}$, $\mathbf{A}_{12} = \mathbf{Y}'(\mathbf{P}_0 - \mathbf{P}_{12})\mathbf{Y}$ where $\mathbf{P}_i$ and $\mathbf{P}_{12}$ represent the projection on ω_i and $\omega_1 \cap \omega_2$ respectively. Then, using Hotelling's T_0^2 and noting that $\mathbf{P}_1 - \mathbf{P}_{12} = \mathbf{P}_0 - \mathbf{P}_2$ (theorem 6.2.1), we have

$$\begin{aligned}
\operatorname{tr}[\mathbf{A}_{12}\mathbf{B}^{-1}] &= \operatorname{tr}[\mathbf{Y}'(\mathbf{P}_0 - \mathbf{P}_{12})\mathbf{Y}\mathbf{B}^{-1}] \\
&= \operatorname{tr}[\mathbf{Y}'(\mathbf{P}_0 - \mathbf{P}_1 + \mathbf{P}_1 - \mathbf{P}_{12})\mathbf{Y}\mathbf{B}^{-1}] \\
&= \operatorname{tr}[\mathbf{Y}'(\mathbf{P}_0 - \mathbf{P}_1 + \mathbf{P}_0 - \mathbf{P}_2)\mathbf{Y}\mathbf{B}^{-1}] \\
&= \operatorname{tr}[\mathbf{A}_1\mathbf{B}^{-1}] + \operatorname{tr}[\mathbf{A}_2\mathbf{B}^{-1}].
\end{aligned}$$

Thus if the separate tests of H_1 and H_2 are well below significance level then both terms on the right-hand side above will be "small". This implies that the left-hand side will also be "small", and the test of $H_1 \wedge H_2$ will be non-significant.

Since orthogonality occurs in multivariate analysis of variance it would seem that in these models, Hotelling's T_0^2 statistic is superior to the U statistic for testing a sequence of hypotheses. Of course now that computers are available, tests of multivariate linear hypotheses are no longer as formidable as they used to be; in particular, the order of nesting is immaterial as on the computer one can test all possible combinations of hypotheses.

9.5 Analysis of covariance

The results of Chapter 7 on univariate analysis of covariance can be easily extended to deal with the analysis of covariance in multivariate linear hypotheses. By considering the analogous equations $\boldsymbol{\theta} = \mathbf{X}\boldsymbol{\beta}$ and $\boldsymbol{\Theta} = \mathbf{X}\mathbf{B}$ (§9.3) we see that the multivariate analogue of

$$E[\mathbf{y}] = \boldsymbol{\theta} + \mathbf{Z}\boldsymbol{\gamma}$$

is simply

$$E[\mathbf{Y}] = \boldsymbol{\Theta} + \mathbf{Z}\boldsymbol{\Lambda}.$$

In §9.1 we showed that a multivariate model is equivalent to a series of univariate models as far as maximum likelihood estimation is concerned, and therefore we have from equations (7.1.3), (7.1.4) and (7.1.2) respectively

$$\tilde{\boldsymbol{\Lambda}}_0 = (\mathbf{Z}'\mathbf{Q}_0\mathbf{Z})^{-1}\mathbf{Z}'\mathbf{Q}_0\mathbf{Y}$$

$$\tilde{\boldsymbol{\Theta}}_0 = \mathbf{P}_0(\mathbf{Y} - \mathbf{Z}\tilde{\boldsymbol{\Lambda}}_0)$$

and

$$\begin{aligned} n\tilde{\boldsymbol{\Sigma}}_0 &= \mathbf{Y}'\tilde{\mathbf{Q}}_0\mathbf{Y} \\ &= \mathbf{Y}'\mathbf{Q}_0\mathbf{Y} - \mathbf{Y}'\mathbf{Q}_0\mathbf{Z}(\mathbf{Z}'\mathbf{Q}_0\mathbf{Z})^{-1}\mathbf{Z}'\mathbf{Q}_0\mathbf{Y} \\ &= n\boldsymbol{\Sigma}_0 - \mathbf{Y}'\mathbf{Q}_0\mathbf{Z}\tilde{\boldsymbol{\Lambda}}_0. \end{aligned}$$

9.6 Additional references

Properties and asymptotic distribution of Hotelling's T_0^2: Ito (1956, 1960), Ghosh (1963), Ito and Schull (1964).

Little has been done on comparing the powers of the different multivariate test statistics; cf. Ito (1962) and Srivastava (1964).

Estimating linear restrictions on regression coefficients: Anderson (1951).

For a general discussion on multivariate techniques, cf. Rao (1952b), Kendall (1957), Roy (1957), and Anderson (1958).

CHAPTER 10

NON-LINEAR REGRESSION

10.1 Notation and assumptions

We now turn our attention to the problem of non-linear regression. For example, suppose we have the following model G

$$E[y_t] = \beta_1 + \beta_2 \exp\{-\gamma x_t\} \quad (t = 1, 2, \ldots, n)$$

and we wish to test the hypothesis H that $\gamma = c$. Although H is a linear hypothesis, G is not linear and no transformation of the y_i's could transform it into a linear model. Not much has been done on the problem of testing such hypotheses and finding *exact* confidence regions for the unknown parameters, and the treatment that we now give is based on Hartley (1961, 1964).

Consider the model

$$y_t = f(\mathbf{x}_t ; \boldsymbol{\theta}) + e_t \quad (t = 1, 2, \ldots, n)$$

where $\boldsymbol{\theta}$ is an unknown m-dimensional parameter, $\mathbf{x}_t = (x_{t1}, x_{t2}, \ldots, x_{tr})'$ is the tth value of an r-dimensional "independent" variable $\mathbf{x}$, and $\mathbf{e}$ is $\mathcal{N}[\mathbf{0}, \sigma^2 \mathbf{I}_n]$. The function f is assumed to be any function satisfying the following conditions:

(a) The partial derivatives

$$f_i(\mathbf{x}; \boldsymbol{\theta}) \equiv \partial f / \partial \theta_i \quad (i = 1, 2, \ldots, m)$$

and

$$f_{ij}(\mathbf{x}; \boldsymbol{\theta}) \equiv \partial^2 f / \partial \theta_i \partial \theta_j \quad (i,j = 1, 2, \ldots, m)$$

are continuous functions of $\boldsymbol{\theta}$ for every $\mathbf{x}$.

(b) Let

$$\mathbf{F}_t' = (f_1(\mathbf{x}_t; \boldsymbol{\theta}), \ldots, f_m(\mathbf{x}_t; \boldsymbol{\theta})).$$

The $n \times m$ matrix $\mathbf{F} = (\mathbf{F}_1, \mathbf{F}_2, \ldots, \mathbf{F}_n)'$ has rank m for any distinct values $\mathbf{x}_1, \mathbf{x}_2, \ldots, \mathbf{x}_n$ and for all $\boldsymbol{\theta}$ in a bounded convex set S of the parameter space. This condition will ensure that certain linear equations derived below will have a unique solution.

(c) Let

$$Q(\boldsymbol{\theta}) = \sum_t (y_t - f(\mathbf{x}_t; \boldsymbol{\theta}))^2 \qquad (10.1.1)$$

and let

$$L = \liminf_{\bar{S}} Q(\boldsymbol{\theta})$$

where $\bar{S}$ is the complement to S in the parameter space. Then it is assumed that it is possible to find a vector $\boldsymbol{\theta}_{(1)}$ in the interior of S such that

$$Q(\boldsymbol{\theta}_{(1)}) < L \, .$$

This last assumption means we can find a region S which we know contains the minimum value of $Q(\boldsymbol{\theta})$ with respect to $\boldsymbol{\theta}$. Then $\boldsymbol{\theta}_{(1)}$ would be a first approximation to this minimum value, $\boldsymbol{\theta}_0$, say.

Finally, in §10.3 we shall use the notation

$$\mathbf{f}(\mathbf{x}; \boldsymbol{\theta}) = (f(\mathbf{x}_1; \boldsymbol{\theta}), \ldots, f(\mathbf{x}_n; \boldsymbol{\theta}))'.$$

10.2 Least squares estimation

If $\boldsymbol{\theta}_{(1)}$ is an approximation to $\boldsymbol{\theta}_0$ we can apply a Taylor expansion to $f(\mathbf{x}; \boldsymbol{\theta})$ and, for $\boldsymbol{\theta}$ in a neighbourhood of $\boldsymbol{\theta}_{(1)}$, obtain the approximate relation

$$Q(\boldsymbol{\theta}) \approx \sum_t \{ y_t - f(\mathbf{x}_t; \boldsymbol{\theta}_{(1)}) - \mathbf{F}'_{t(1)}(\boldsymbol{\theta} - \boldsymbol{\theta}_{(1)}) \}^2 \qquad (10.2.1)$$

where $\mathbf{F}_{t(1)}$ denotes $\mathbf{F}_t$ evaluated at $\boldsymbol{\theta} = \boldsymbol{\theta}_{(1)}$. Putting $z_t = y_t - f(\mathbf{x}_t; \boldsymbol{\theta}_{(1)})$ and $\boldsymbol{\beta} = \boldsymbol{\theta} - \boldsymbol{\theta}_{(1)}$, equation (10.2.1) becomes

$$Q(\boldsymbol{\theta}) \approx (\mathbf{z} - \mathbf{F}_{(1)}\boldsymbol{\beta})'(\mathbf{z} - \mathbf{F}_{(1)}\boldsymbol{\beta}) \, .$$

Since $\mathbf{F}_{(1)}$ has rank m (by assumption (b)), the $m \times m$ matrix $\mathbf{F}'_{(1)}\mathbf{F}_{(1)}$ will be non-singular, and therefore the least squares estimate $\boldsymbol{\beta}_{(1)}$ of $\boldsymbol{\beta}$ for the above quadratic expression is simply

$$\boldsymbol{\beta}_{(1)} = (\mathbf{F}'_{(1)}\mathbf{F}_{(1)})^{-1}\mathbf{F}_{(1)}\mathbf{z} \, .$$

Also $\boldsymbol{\beta}_{(1)}$ will be an estimate of $\boldsymbol{\theta}_0 - \boldsymbol{\theta}_{(1)}$ and therefore the "correction" to $\boldsymbol{\theta}_{(1)}$ is approximately $\boldsymbol{\beta}_{(1)}$. Thus our new approximation to $\boldsymbol{\theta}_0$ is

$$\boldsymbol{\theta}_{(2)} = \boldsymbol{\beta}_{(1)} + \boldsymbol{\theta}_{(1)}$$

and we can repeat this so-called Gauss–Newton iterative procedure and obtain further approximations $\boldsymbol{\theta}_{(3)}$, $\boldsymbol{\theta}_{(4)}$, etc., until the correction becomes negligible.

There are several difficulties associated with this method, and in particular the problem of convergence of the successive approximations.

For example, when $Q(\boldsymbol{\theta})$ is very flat near $\boldsymbol{\theta}_0$, the process may oscillate about $\boldsymbol{\theta}_0$. To overcome this, Hartley (1961) suggests the following modification of the method.

Consider the function

$$Q(v) = Q(\boldsymbol{\theta}_{(1)} + v\boldsymbol{\beta}_{(1)}) \quad 0 \leqslant v \leqslant 1$$

and let v_1 be the value of v which minimises $Q(v)$ on the interval $0 \leqslant v \leqslant 1$. Our new approximation is now

$$\boldsymbol{\theta}_{(2)} = \boldsymbol{\theta}_{(1)} + v_1\boldsymbol{\beta}_{(1)}$$

and it follows that

$$Q(\boldsymbol{\theta}_{(2)}) \leqslant Q(\boldsymbol{\theta}_{(1)}) < L$$

so that $\boldsymbol{\theta}_{(2)}$ is an interior point of S. It is obvious that this procedure will give us convergence to a solution of $\partial Q(\boldsymbol{\theta})/\partial\theta_i = 0 \;\; (i = 1, 2, \ldots, m)$.

This raises our next problem, for there may be more than one stationary point in S. However, Hartley shows that if we make the additional assumption (d) that the matrix with i,jth element $\partial^2 Q(\boldsymbol{\theta})/\partial\theta_i\,\partial\theta_j$ is positive definite in S, then there is only one stationary point in S, and by assumption (c) this will be the absolute minimum $\boldsymbol{\theta}_0$ of $Q(\boldsymbol{\theta})$.

Finally we note that there is the problem of finding a region S and an initial approximation $\boldsymbol{\theta}_{(1)}$ in S satisfying assumption (c). Various *ad hoc* methods are described in Hartley (1948), Williams (1959), and Turner *et al.* (1961), and although no general method can be prescribed we can, with the advent of the computer, "search" the parameter space for a suitable S. Stevens (1951) has pointed out that any element θ_i of $\boldsymbol{\theta}$ which appears "linearly" in $f(\mathbf{x}; \boldsymbol{\theta})$ does not require an initial approximation. We can demonstrate this from an example given by Williams (1962).

Example. Let

$$E[y_t] = \theta_1 + \theta_2 f(x_t, \theta_3),$$

then if c_1 is a trial approximation to c_0, the least squares estimate of θ_3, we have approximately

$$Q(\boldsymbol{\theta}) = \sum_t \{y_t - \theta_1 - \theta_2[f(x_t, c_1) - (\theta_3 - c_1) f_1(x_t, c_1)]\}^2$$

and minimising this gives a first approximation for $\boldsymbol{\theta}_0$.

In concluding this section we shall briefly mention the problem of finding the mean and the variance matrix of $\boldsymbol{\theta}_0$. We note that from the normality assumptions on the errors, $\boldsymbol{\theta}_0$ is also the maximum likelihood estimate of $\boldsymbol{\theta}$. Therefore as $n \to \infty$, $\boldsymbol{\theta}_0$ will have the usual asymptotic properties of consistency, efficiency and normality (under reasonable assumptions about f) and asymptotic confidence intervals could be found for the elements of $\boldsymbol{\theta}$. However, in practice, n will usually be of moderate size and the asymptotic approach may not be satisfactory.

Therefore in the next section we shall consider methods for finding *exact* confidence regions.

10.3 Confidence intervals and hypothesis testing

From the identity

$$\mathbf{e}'\mathbf{e} = \mathbf{e}'\mathbf{P}\mathbf{e} + \mathbf{e}'(\mathbf{I} - \mathbf{P})\mathbf{e}$$

where $\mathbf{P}$ is any symmetric, idempotent matrix of rank p, we have from Cochran's theorem (4.2.2) that

$$F_{p,n-p} = \frac{(n-p)}{p}\,\frac{\mathbf{e}'\mathbf{P}\mathbf{e}}{\mathbf{e}'(\mathbf{I}-\mathbf{P})\mathbf{e}} \tag{10.3.1}$$

$$= \frac{(n-p)}{p}\,\frac{(\mathbf{y} - \mathbf{f}(\mathbf{x};\boldsymbol{\theta}))'\mathbf{P}(\mathbf{y} - \mathbf{f}(\mathbf{x};\boldsymbol{\theta}))}{(\mathbf{y} - \mathbf{f}(\mathbf{x};\boldsymbol{\theta}))'(\mathbf{I}-\mathbf{P})(\mathbf{y} - \mathbf{f}(\mathbf{x};\boldsymbol{\theta}))}$$

has the F distribution with p, n-p degrees of freedom. Thus if $F_{p,n-p}(\alpha)$ is the upper 100α per cent of F, then

$$F_{p,n-p} \leqslant F_{p,n-p}(\alpha) \tag{10.3.2}$$

provides a 100α per cent confidence region for $\boldsymbol{\theta}$. In particular we can test the hypothesis $\boldsymbol{\theta} = \mathbf{c}$ by simply putting $\boldsymbol{\theta}$ equal to $\mathbf{c}$ in (10.3.1) and seeing if this value of F is greater than $F_{p,n-p}(\alpha)$. If it is, then we reject the hypothesis at the 100α per cent level of significance.

In using (10.3.1) to find a confidence region for $\boldsymbol{\theta}$ we would endeavour to choose $\mathbf{P}$ so that the corresponding region would be as simple as possible. Two criteria for choosing $\mathbf{P}$ have been suggested. The first, due to Williams (1962) and Halperin (1963), is to choose $\mathbf{P}$ so that $F_{p,n-p} = 0$ when $\boldsymbol{\theta} = \boldsymbol{\theta}_0$. Now the least squares equations are

$$\sum_t \{(y_t - f(\mathbf{x}_t;\boldsymbol{\theta}_0))\, f_j(\mathbf{x}_t;\boldsymbol{\theta}_0)\} = 0 \quad (j = 1, 2, \ldots, m)$$

or

$$\mathbf{F}'_{(0)}(\mathbf{y} - \mathbf{f}(\mathbf{x};\boldsymbol{\theta}_0)) = \mathbf{0}.$$

Thus if we choose $\mathbf{P} = \mathbf{F}(\mathbf{F}'\mathbf{F})^{-1}\mathbf{F}'$, then $(\mathbf{y} - \mathbf{f}(\mathbf{x};\boldsymbol{\theta}))'\mathbf{P}(\mathbf{y} - \mathbf{f}(\mathbf{x};\boldsymbol{\theta}))$ is zero when $\boldsymbol{\theta} = \boldsymbol{\theta}_0$. The main disadvantage of this choice of $\mathbf{P}$ is that the denominator of $F_{p,n-p}$ may be a complicated function of $\boldsymbol{\theta}$ and the confidence region will be difficult to construct. Therefore an alternative criterion, suggested by Hartley (1964), is to choose $\mathbf{P}$ such that the denominator is independent of $\boldsymbol{\theta}$ or as "near" independent as possible. This could be achieved if $\mathbf{f}(\mathbf{x};\boldsymbol{\theta})$ took the form $\mathbf{Z}\boldsymbol{\gamma}$, where $\mathbf{Z}$ is independent of $\boldsymbol{\theta}$ and the elements of $\boldsymbol{\gamma}$ are functions of $\boldsymbol{\theta}$. For then, choosing $\mathbf{P} = \mathbf{Z}(\mathbf{Z}'\mathbf{Z})^{-1}\mathbf{Z}'$, gives

$$\mathbf{e}'(\mathbf{I} - \mathbf{P})\mathbf{e} = \mathbf{y}'(\mathbf{I} - \mathbf{P})\mathbf{y}$$

which is independent of $\boldsymbol{\theta}$. Therefore the closer we can approximate $f(\mathbf{x}; \boldsymbol{\theta})$ by the form $\mathbf{Z}\boldsymbol{\gamma}$, the less will the denominator of $F_{p,n-p}$ depend on $\boldsymbol{\theta}$.

Looking at it another way,

$$\begin{aligned} \mathbf{e}'\mathbf{P}\mathbf{e} &= \mathbf{e}'\mathbf{e} - \mathbf{e}'(\mathbf{I} - \mathbf{P})\mathbf{e} \\ &= \mathbf{e}'\mathbf{e} - \mathbf{y}'(\mathbf{I} - \mathbf{P})\mathbf{y} \end{aligned}$$

and therefore, as far as $\boldsymbol{\theta}$ is concerned, (10.3.2) is equivalent to $\mathbf{e}'\mathbf{e} \leqslant$ constant. Thus Hartley's method is to choose $\mathbf{P}$ such that the contours of $\mathbf{e}'\mathbf{P}\mathbf{e} = d_1$ closely approximate to the set of contours $\mathbf{e}'\mathbf{e} = d_2$ of constant likelihood.

Although the best approximation $\mathbf{Z}\boldsymbol{\gamma}$ to use will usually depend on the form $f(\mathbf{x}; \boldsymbol{\theta})$, some general methods are available, and Hartley (1964) gives one based on Lagrangian interpolation. However, much more work needs to be done in investigating the confidence regions obtained in particular examples; some of the difficulties which can arise are discussed in Williams (1962). Another problem is that of finding confidence regions for subsets of the elements of $\boldsymbol{\theta}$. Such confidence regions would also provide tests of sub-hypotheses, and an example of this is given in Halperin (1963). Suppose $E[\mathbf{y}] = \mathbf{X}\boldsymbol{\alpha}$ where $\boldsymbol{\alpha} = (\theta_1, \theta_2, \ldots, \theta_k)'$ and the elements of $\mathbf{X}$ are functions of $\boldsymbol{\delta} = (\theta_{k+1}, \theta_{k+2}, \ldots, \theta_m)'$ in which each θ_{k+j} occurs in one and only one column of $\mathbf{X}$. Then Halperin shows how to construct a confidence region for $\boldsymbol{\delta}$ only and thus provide a test for $\boldsymbol{\delta} = \mathbf{c}$, say.

Finally we would mention a recent paper by Halperin (1964) in which he considers a generalisation of the above work to the case when the observations y_t are now vectors from a multi-normal distribution with general variance matrix $\boldsymbol{\Sigma}$.

CHAPTER 11

LARGE SAMPLE THEORY FOR NON-LINEAR HYPOTHESES

11.1 Introduction

Suppose we are given N independent observations $x_1, x_2, \ldots, x_N$ (these may be vectors) from a known probability density function $p(x, \boldsymbol{\theta})$, where $\boldsymbol{\theta}' = (\theta_1, \ldots, \theta_n)$ and $\boldsymbol{\theta}$ is known to belong to W_0, a subset of E_n. We wish to test whether or not $\boldsymbol{\theta}_t$, the true value of $\boldsymbol{\theta}$, belongs to W_1, a subset of W_0, given that N is large. As in linear theory, there are two ways of specifying W_0 and W_1; either in the form of constraint equations such as $\mathbf{a}(\boldsymbol{\theta}) = (a_1(\boldsymbol{\theta}), \ldots, a_r(\boldsymbol{\theta}))' = \mathbf{0}$, or in the form of freedom equations $\boldsymbol{\theta} = \boldsymbol{\theta}(\boldsymbol{\alpha})$ where $\boldsymbol{\alpha}' = (\alpha_1, \ldots, \alpha_{n-r})$, or perhaps by a combination of both constraint and freedom equations. Although to any freedom-equation specification there will correspond a constraint-equation specification and vice versa, this relationship is often difficult to derive in practice, and therefore the two forms of specification are usually dealt with separately.

Three methods of testing $\boldsymbol{\theta}_t \in W_1$ are available: the likelihood ratio test, the Wald test (Wald, 1943), and the Lagrangian multiplier test (Rao, 1947 and Silvey, 1959). The choice of which method to use will largely depend on the ease of computation of the test statistic and therefore to some extent on the method of specification of W_1. In what follows we shall consider the constraint equation form $\mathbf{a}(\boldsymbol{\theta}) = \mathbf{0}$ only; thus $W_1 = \{\boldsymbol{\theta} : \mathbf{a}(\boldsymbol{\theta}) = \mathbf{0} \text{ and } \boldsymbol{\theta} \in W_0\}$.

The aim of this chapter is to show how this non-linear hypothesis and non-normal model can be approximated, for large N, by a linear model and linear hypothesis. We shall then use this approximation to define the three test statistics mentioned above and to show that they are equivalent test statistics asymptotically. But first we need some notation.

11.2 Notation

Let $L_N(\boldsymbol{\theta}) = \prod_{j=1}^{N} p(x_j, \boldsymbol{\theta})$ represent the likelihood function, and for $i = 0, 1$, let $\boldsymbol{\theta}_i$ be the maximum likelihood estimate of $\boldsymbol{\theta}$ for $\boldsymbol{\theta} \in W_i$; we note that $\boldsymbol{\theta}_i$ depends on N, but we drop it from the notation for simplicity. The information matrix is denoted by $\mathbf{B}_\theta$ where $\mathbf{B}_\theta$ is the positive definite matrix with i,jth element

$$-\frac{1}{N}E\left[\frac{\partial^2 \log L_N(\boldsymbol{\theta})}{\partial\theta_i\,\partial\theta_j}\right] = -E\left[\frac{\partial^2 \log p(x,\boldsymbol{\theta})}{\partial\theta_i\,\partial\theta_j}\right].$$

Let $\mathbf{D}\log L_N(\boldsymbol{\theta})$ be the column vector with ith element $\partial \log L_N(\boldsymbol{\theta})/\partial\theta_i$, and let $\mathbf{A}_\theta$ be the $n \times r$ matrix with i,jth element $\partial a_j(\boldsymbol{\theta})/\partial\theta_i$. For any function $g(\boldsymbol{\theta})$, $\mathbf{D}^2 g(\boldsymbol{\theta})$ is the matrix with i,jth element $\partial^2 g(\boldsymbol{\theta})/\partial\theta_i\,\partial\theta_j$.

We now assume that W_0, W_1, p and $\mathbf{a}(\boldsymbol{\theta})$ satisfy certain regularity assumptions which we list below (Silvey, 1959). These are not the weakest assumptions we could use, but are probably the simplest for the development given here.

(i) $\boldsymbol{\theta}_t$ is an interior point of W_0.

(ii) For every $\boldsymbol{\theta} \in W_0$, $z(\boldsymbol{\theta}) = \int(\log p(x,\boldsymbol{\theta}))\,p(x,\boldsymbol{\theta}_t)dx$ exists.

(iii) W_0 is a convex compact subset of E_n.

(iv) For almost all x, $\log p(x,\boldsymbol{\theta})$ is continuous on W_0.

(v) For almost all x and for every $\boldsymbol{\theta} \in W_0$, $\partial \log p(x,\boldsymbol{\theta})/\partial\theta_i$ $(i = 1, 2, \ldots, n)$ exists and $|\partial \log p(x,\boldsymbol{\theta})/\partial\theta_i| < g(x)$ $(i = 1, 2, \ldots, n)$ where $\int g(x)p(x,\boldsymbol{\theta}_t)dx < \infty$.

(vi) The function $\mathbf{a}(\boldsymbol{\theta})$ is continuous on W_0.

(vii) There exists a point $\boldsymbol{\theta}_* \in W_1$ such that $z(\boldsymbol{\theta}_*) > z(\boldsymbol{\theta})$ when $\boldsymbol{\theta} \in W_1$ and $\boldsymbol{\theta} \neq \boldsymbol{\theta}_*$.

(viii) $\boldsymbol{\theta}_*$ is an interior point of W_1.

(ix) The functions $a_i(\boldsymbol{\theta})$ possess first- and second-order partial derivatives which are continuous (and therefore bounded) on W_0.

(x) The order of the operations of integration and differentiation with respect to $\boldsymbol{\theta}$ are reversible; thus

$$0 = (\partial/\partial\theta_i)\int p(x,\boldsymbol{\theta})\,dx = \int \partial p/\partial\theta_i\,dx$$

and

$$0 = \int \partial^2 p/\partial\theta_i\,\partial\theta_j\,dx.$$

(xi) For almost all x the function $\log p(x,\boldsymbol{\theta})$ possesses continuous second-order partial derivatives in a neighbourhood of $\boldsymbol{\theta}_t$. Also, if $\boldsymbol{\theta}$ belongs to this neighbourhood, then

$$|\partial^2 \log p(x,\boldsymbol{\theta})/\partial\theta_i\,\partial\theta_j| < G_1(x) \quad \text{for } i,j = 1, 2, \ldots, n$$

where $\int G_1(x)p(x,\boldsymbol{\theta}_t)dx < \infty$.

(xii) For almost all x, $\log p(x,\boldsymbol{\theta})$ possesses third-order partial derivatives in a neighbourhood of $\boldsymbol{\theta}_t$, and if $\boldsymbol{\theta}$ is in this neighbourhood, then

$$|\partial^3 \log p(x, \boldsymbol{\theta})/\partial\theta_i\, \partial\theta_j\, \partial\theta_k| < G_2(x)$$

where $\int G_2(x)\, p(x, \boldsymbol{\theta}_t)\, dx < \infty$.

(xiii) The matrix $\mathbf{B}_\theta$ exists and is positive definite in a neighbourhood of $\boldsymbol{\theta}_t$; also its elements are continuous functions of $\boldsymbol{\theta}$ there.

(xiv) The matrix $\mathbf{A}_\theta$ has rank r in the neighbourhood of $\boldsymbol{\theta}_t$.

In the above assumptions, the statement "for almost all x" means "for all x except for a set of measure zero – the probability measure being defined by the (cumulative) distribution function of $p(x, \boldsymbol{\theta})$". Also these assumptions can be applied to discontinuous densities p by writing the above integrals in the Stieltjes form.

Assumptions (ix), (xiii) and (xiv) imply that $[\mathbf{A}\,\mathbf{B}^{-1}\mathbf{A}']_\theta$ is positive definite and its elements are continuous functions of $\boldsymbol{\theta}$ in the neighbourhood of $\boldsymbol{\theta}_t$ (Appendix 1, lemma 2).

The matrices $\mathbf{B}_t$, $\mathbf{B}_0$, $\mathbf{B}_1$, $\mathbf{B}_*$, denote that $\mathbf{B}_\theta$ is evaluated at $\boldsymbol{\theta}_t$, $\boldsymbol{\theta}_0$, $\boldsymbol{\theta}_1$ and $\boldsymbol{\theta}_*$ respectively.

Finally we require the following definitions (cf. Mann and Wald (1943)). If $\{\mathbf{z}_N\}$ is a sequence of random vectors we write $p\lim \mathbf{z}_N = \mathbf{0}$ if, for every $\epsilon > 0$,

$$\lim_{N\to\infty} \Pr[\|\mathbf{z}_N\| \leqslant \epsilon] = 1.$$

Also if $g(N)$ is a positive function of N, we write $\mathbf{z}_N = \mathbf{o}_p[g(N)]$ if $p\lim \mathbf{z}_N/g(N) = \mathbf{0}$, and $\mathbf{z}_N = \mathbf{0}_p[g(N)]$ if for each $\epsilon > 0$ there exists an $A(\epsilon) > 0$ such that

$$\Pr[\|\mathbf{z}_N\| \leqslant A(\epsilon)\, g(N)] \geqslant 1 - \epsilon$$

for all values of N.

11.3 Maximum likelihood equations

From assumptions (iii) to (v) it can be shown, using the Strong Law of Large Numbers, that for almost all sequences $\{x\} = x_1, x_2, \ldots,$ the sequence $N^{-1} \log L_N(\boldsymbol{\theta})$ converges to $z(\boldsymbol{\theta})$ uniformly with respect to $\boldsymbol{\theta}$ in W_0. Assumption (iii) ensures that any continuous function on W_0 attains its supremum at some point in W_0. In particular the function $\log L_N(\boldsymbol{\theta})$, for almost all x, attains its supremum in W_0 at $\boldsymbol{\theta}_0$, the maximum likelihood estimate. But from Wald (1949), $z(\boldsymbol{\theta}_t) > z(\boldsymbol{\theta})$ when $\boldsymbol{\theta} \neq \boldsymbol{\theta}_t$ and $\boldsymbol{\theta} \in W_0$, and therefore it can be shown that $\boldsymbol{\theta}_0$ (which depends on N) converges to $\boldsymbol{\theta}_t$ for almost all $\{x\}$ as N tends to infinity.

In other words we say that $\boldsymbol{\theta}_0 \to \boldsymbol{\theta}_t$ with probability one as $N \to \infty$, which implies the weaker statement $p\lim(\boldsymbol{\theta}_0 - \boldsymbol{\theta}_t) = 0$. Since $\boldsymbol{\theta}_t$ is an interior point (assumption (i)) it follows that for N sufficiently large, $\boldsymbol{\theta}_0$ will also be an interior point of W_0 and will, by the usual laws of calculus, emerge as a solution of

$$\mathbf{D} N^{-1} \log L_N(\boldsymbol{\theta}) = \mathbf{0}.$$

Using a Taylor expansion, we have from assumption (xii)

$$\mathbf{0} = \mathbf{D} N^{-1} \log L_N(\boldsymbol{\theta}_t) + [\mathbf{D}^2 N^{-1} \log L_N(\boldsymbol{\theta}_t)](\boldsymbol{\theta}_0 - \boldsymbol{\theta}_t) + \mathbf{o}_p(1).$$

But by assumption (xi), the Law of Large Numbers and assumption (x),

$$p\lim \mathbf{D}^2 N^{-1} \log L_N(\boldsymbol{\theta}_t) = \mathbf{D}^2 z(\boldsymbol{\theta}_t) = -\mathbf{B}_t.$$

Thus we write

$$\mathbf{D}^2 N^{-1} \log L_N(\boldsymbol{\theta}_t) = -\mathbf{B}_t + \mathbf{o}_p(1) \qquad (11.3.1)$$

and hence

$$\boldsymbol{\theta}_0 - \boldsymbol{\theta}_t = \mathbf{B}_t^{-1} \mathbf{D} N^{-1} \log L_N(\boldsymbol{\theta}_t) + \mathbf{o}_p(1).$$

Now from assumption (x)

$$E\left[\frac{\partial \log p(x, \boldsymbol{\theta}_t)}{\partial \theta_i}\right] = \int \frac{\partial(x, \boldsymbol{\theta}_t)}{\partial \theta_i} \frac{1}{p}\, p\, dx$$
$$= 0$$

and therefore from the multivariate form of the central limit theorem (cf. Cramér, 1963), $N^{\frac{1}{2}} \mathbf{D} N^{-1} \log L_N(\boldsymbol{\theta}_t)$ is asymptotically $\mathcal{N}[\mathbf{0}, \mathbf{B}_t]$. This implies that $N^{\frac{1}{2}}(\boldsymbol{\theta}_0 - \boldsymbol{\theta}_t)$ is asymptotically

$$\mathcal{N}[\mathbf{0}, \mathbf{B}_t^{-1}] \qquad (11.3.2)$$

and since $\mathbf{B}_t^{-1}$ does not depend on N we have

$$N^{\frac{1}{2}}(\boldsymbol{\theta}_0 - \boldsymbol{\theta}_t) = \mathbf{0}_p(1). \qquad (11.3.3)$$

We now turn our attention to $\boldsymbol{\theta}_1$ and first of all make one further assumption:

(xv) If H is not true then $\boldsymbol{\theta}_t$ is "near" W_1. This means that since $\boldsymbol{\theta}_t$ and $\boldsymbol{\theta}_*$ maximise $z(\boldsymbol{\theta})$ for $\boldsymbol{\theta}$ belonging to W_0 and W_1 respectively, $\boldsymbol{\theta}_t$ will be "near" $\boldsymbol{\theta}_*$. We define what we mean by nearness by

$$N^{\frac{1}{2}}(\boldsymbol{\theta}_t - \boldsymbol{\theta}_*) = \mathbf{0}(1) \qquad (11.3.4)$$

and therefore in testing H we now consider classes of alternatives $\boldsymbol{\theta}_t$

which tend to W_1 as $N \to \infty$. This idea is discussed in Neyman (1959) and in his terminology we have from (11.3.3) that $\boldsymbol{\theta}_0$ is a weakly root N consistent estimate of $\boldsymbol{\theta}_t$. The reason why such a class of alternatives is chosen is that for a fixed alternative, $\boldsymbol{\theta}_t$, the power of the tests to be considered will tend to unity as N tends to infinity.

Assumption (xv) now implies that assumptions (xi) to (xiii) inclusive are valid for a neighbourhood of $\boldsymbol{\theta}_*$, and from assumptions (iii) and (vi) it follows that W_1 is a convex compact subset of W_0. Therefore, by a similar argument to that which led to equation (11.3.3) we have (cf. Silvey (1959), p. 394)

$$N^{\frac{1}{2}}(\boldsymbol{\theta}_1 - \boldsymbol{\theta}_*) = 0_p(1) \tag{11.3.5}$$

In addition, as $\boldsymbol{\theta}_*$ is an interior point of W_1, $\boldsymbol{\theta}_1$ will be an interior point also, for large enough N, and will emerge as a solution of (cf. §1.6)

$$\mathbf{D}N^{-1}\log L_N(\boldsymbol{\theta}_1) + \mathbf{A}_1\boldsymbol{\mu} = \mathbf{0} \tag{11.3.6}$$

and

$$\mathbf{a}(\boldsymbol{\theta}_1) = \mathbf{0} \tag{11.3.7}$$

where $\boldsymbol{\mu}$ is the Lagrange multiplier.

Finally from equations (11.3.3) to (11.3.5) we see that $\boldsymbol{\theta}_t$, $\boldsymbol{\theta}_0$, $\boldsymbol{\theta}_1$ and $\boldsymbol{\theta}_*$ are all "near" each other. Since $\mathbf{A}_\theta$ and $\mathbf{B}_\theta$ are continuous functions of $\boldsymbol{\theta}$ in the neighbourhood of $\boldsymbol{\theta}_t$, we have from Taylor expansions

$$\mathbf{B}_0 = \mathbf{B}_t + 0_p(N^{-\frac{1}{2}})$$

$$\mathbf{A}_* = \mathbf{A}_t + 0(N^{-\frac{1}{2}})$$

and

$$\mathbf{A}_1 = \mathbf{A}_t + 0_p(N^{-\frac{1}{2}}).$$

11.4 The linear model approximation

Using the asymptotic results above, we can now show that our original hypothesis and model can be approximated by the linear model

$$\mathbf{y} = \boldsymbol{\phi} + \mathbf{e},$$

where $\mathbf{e}$ is $\mathcal{N}[\mathbf{0}, \mathbf{I}_n]$, and the linear hypothesis

$$H : \omega = N[(\mathbf{A}'\mathbf{V})_t]$$

where $\mathbf{V}_t$ is defined later. The argument is as follows.

Since $N^{\frac{1}{2}}(\boldsymbol{\theta}_1 - \boldsymbol{\theta}_0) = 0_p(1)$ we have, using a Taylor expansion and applying (11.3.1) to a neighbourhood of $\boldsymbol{\theta}_t$,

$$\mathbf{D}N^{-1}\log L_N(\boldsymbol{\theta}_1) = \mathbf{D}N^{-1}\log L_N(\boldsymbol{\theta}_0) + [\mathbf{D}^2N^{-1}\log L_N(\boldsymbol{\theta}_0)](\boldsymbol{\theta}_1 - \boldsymbol{\theta}_0) + 0_p(N^{-1})$$

$$= - \mathbf{B}_0(\boldsymbol{\theta}_1 - \boldsymbol{\theta}_0) + \mathbf{0}_p(N^{-1}),$$
$$= - \mathbf{B}_t(\boldsymbol{\theta}_1 - \boldsymbol{\theta}_0) + \mathbf{0}_p(N^{-1}).$$

Therefore, from equation (11.3.6),

$$\mathbf{A}_1 N^{\frac{1}{2}}\boldsymbol{\mu} = - N^{\frac{1}{2}}\mathbf{D}N^{-1} \log L_N(\boldsymbol{\theta}_1)$$
$$= \mathbf{0}_p(1)$$

which means that we can write

$$\mathbf{A}_t N^{\frac{1}{2}}\boldsymbol{\mu} = \mathbf{A}_1 N^{\frac{1}{2}}\boldsymbol{\mu} + \mathbf{o}_p(1). \tag{11.4.1}$$

Thus (11.3.6) becomes

$$\mathbf{B}_t N^{\frac{1}{2}}(\boldsymbol{\theta}_0 - \boldsymbol{\theta}_*) - \mathbf{B}_t N^{\frac{1}{2}}(\boldsymbol{\theta}_1 - \boldsymbol{\theta}_*) + \mathbf{A}_t N^{\frac{1}{2}}\boldsymbol{\mu} = \mathbf{o}_p(1) \tag{11.4.2}$$

and in the same way

$$\mathbf{0} = N^{\frac{1}{2}}[\mathbf{a}(\boldsymbol{\theta}_1) - \mathbf{a}(\boldsymbol{\theta}_*)]$$
$$= \mathbf{A}'_* N^{\frac{1}{2}}(\boldsymbol{\theta}_1 - \boldsymbol{\theta}_*) + \mathbf{0}_p(N^{-\frac{1}{2}})$$
$$= \mathbf{A}'_t N^{\frac{1}{2}}(\boldsymbol{\theta}_1 - \boldsymbol{\theta}_*) + \mathbf{0}_p(N^{-\frac{1}{2}}).$$

Therefore (11.3.7) becomes

$$\mathbf{A}'_t N^{\frac{1}{2}}(\boldsymbol{\theta}_1 - \boldsymbol{\theta}_*) = \mathbf{o}_p(1). \tag{11.4.3}$$

Now from (11.3.2),

$$N^{\frac{1}{2}}(\boldsymbol{\theta}_0 - \boldsymbol{\theta}_*) = N^{\frac{1}{2}}(\boldsymbol{\theta}_t - \boldsymbol{\theta}_*) + \boldsymbol{\delta} \tag{11.4.4}$$

where $\boldsymbol{\delta}$ is $\mathcal{N}[\mathbf{0}, \mathbf{B}_t^{-1}]$, and this reminds us of the linear model given in § 2.3. As $\mathbf{B}_t$ is positive definite so is $\mathbf{B}_t^{-1}$, and by Appendix 1 (lemma 1), there exists a non-singular matrix $\mathbf{V}_t$ such that $\mathbf{B}_t^{-1} = \mathbf{V}_t\mathbf{V}'_t$. Putting

$$\left.\begin{aligned} \mathbf{y} &= N^{\frac{1}{2}}\mathbf{V}_t^{-1}(\boldsymbol{\theta}_0 - \boldsymbol{\theta}_*) \\ \boldsymbol{\phi} &= N^{\frac{1}{2}}\mathbf{V}_t^{-1}(\boldsymbol{\theta}_t - \boldsymbol{\theta}_*) \\ \text{and} \quad \boldsymbol{\phi}_1 &= N^{\frac{1}{2}}\mathbf{V}_t^{-1}(\boldsymbol{\theta}_1 - \boldsymbol{\theta}_*) \end{aligned}\right\} \tag{11.4.5}$$

in equation (11.4.4) leads to the linear model

$$\mathbf{y} = \boldsymbol{\phi} + \mathbf{e},$$

where $\mathbf{e}$ is $\mathcal{N}[\mathbf{0}, \mathbf{I}_n]$ Equations (11.4.2) and (11.4.3) become

$$\mathbf{y} - \boldsymbol{\phi}_1 + [\mathbf{A}'\mathbf{V}]'_t N^{\frac{1}{2}}\boldsymbol{\mu} = \mathbf{o}_p(1)$$

and

$$[\mathbf{A}'\mathbf{V}]_t \boldsymbol{\phi}_1 = \mathbf{o}_p(1).$$

But these are precisely the least squares equations for testing the linear hypothesis $[\mathbf{A}'\mathbf{V}]_t \boldsymbol{\phi} = \mathbf{0}$. Thus our original model is asymptotically equivalent to a linear model with $\mathbf{G}:\Omega = E_n$ and $H:\omega = N[(\mathbf{A}'\mathbf{V}_t)\ ]$.

This asymptotic equivalence to a linear hypothesis also holds for hypotheses expressed in the freedom equation form. Suppose that W_1 is expressed in the freedom equation form described in §11.1, then $W_1 = \{\boldsymbol{\theta} : \boldsymbol{\theta} = \boldsymbol{\theta}(\boldsymbol{\alpha})\}$. Let $\boldsymbol{\Theta}_\alpha$ be the $n-r \times n$ matrix with i,jth element $\partial\theta_j/\partial\alpha_i$ and let $\boldsymbol{\alpha}_*$ be defined by $\boldsymbol{\theta}_* = \boldsymbol{\theta}(\boldsymbol{\alpha}_*)$. We assume that $\boldsymbol{\theta}$ is a one-to-one function of $\boldsymbol{\alpha}$, so that $\boldsymbol{\alpha}_*$ is unique and the rank of $\boldsymbol{\Theta}_\alpha$ is $n-r$. Then, provided certain regularity conditions hold on $\boldsymbol{\theta}(\boldsymbol{\alpha})$, it can be shown (Seber 1964c), by using a similar algebra to that above, that the linear hypothesis approximation is now $H:\boldsymbol{\phi} = \mathbf{V}_t^{-1}\boldsymbol{\Theta}_*\boldsymbol{\gamma}$, where $\boldsymbol{\Theta}_*$ is $\boldsymbol{\Theta}_\alpha$ evaluated at $\boldsymbol{\alpha} = \boldsymbol{\alpha}_*$. Also in this paper it is shown how the theory can be modified to take care of the case when $\mathbf{B}_t$ is singular.

11.5 The three test statistics

Consider the linear model $\mathbf{y} = \boldsymbol{\phi} + \mathbf{e}$, where $\mathbf{e}$ is $\mathcal{N}[\mathbf{0}, \mathbf{I}_n]$, $G:\boldsymbol{\phi} \in \Omega$, and $H:\boldsymbol{\phi} \in \Omega \cap N(\mathbf{C})$ for some matrix $\mathbf{C}$. To find $\boldsymbol{\phi}_1$ we minimise $\|\mathbf{y} - \boldsymbol{\phi}\|^2$ subject to $\mathbf{C}\boldsymbol{\phi} = \mathbf{0}$ and $(\mathbf{I} - \mathbf{P}_0)\boldsymbol{\phi} = \mathbf{0}$. Introducing Lagrange multipliers $-\frac{1}{2}\boldsymbol{\lambda}$ and $-\frac{1}{2}\boldsymbol{\lambda}_1$, we have (cf. equation (3.4.2))

$$\mathbf{y} - \boldsymbol{\phi}_1 + \mathbf{C}'\boldsymbol{\lambda} + (\mathbf{I} - \mathbf{P}_0)\boldsymbol{\lambda}_1 = \mathbf{0} \qquad (11.5.1)$$

and

$$\mathbf{C}\boldsymbol{\phi}_1 = \mathbf{0} \quad \text{and} \quad (\mathbf{I} - \mathbf{P}_0)\boldsymbol{\phi}_1 = \mathbf{0}. \qquad (11.5.2)$$

Premultiplying (11.5.1) by $\mathbf{P}_0$ and using (11.5.2) leads to

$$\begin{bmatrix} \mathbf{I}_n , & -\mathbf{P}_0\mathbf{C}' \\ -\mathbf{C}\mathbf{P}_0 , & \mathbf{0} \end{bmatrix} \begin{bmatrix} \boldsymbol{\phi}_1 \\ \boldsymbol{\lambda} \end{bmatrix} = \begin{bmatrix} \mathbf{P}_0\mathbf{y} \\ \mathbf{0} \end{bmatrix}.$$

By choosing $\mathbf{C}$ correctly (§4.3), $[\mathbf{C}\mathbf{P}_0\mathbf{C}']^{-1}$ will exist, and the matrix on the left-hand side above can be inverted to give

$$\boldsymbol{\phi}_1 = [\mathbf{P}_0 - \mathbf{P}_0\mathbf{C}'(\mathbf{C}\mathbf{P}_0\mathbf{C}')^{-1}\mathbf{C}\mathbf{P}_0]\mathbf{y} = \mathbf{P}_1\mathbf{y}$$

and

$$\boldsymbol{\lambda} = -(\mathbf{C}\mathbf{P}_0\mathbf{C}')^{-1}\mathbf{C}\mathbf{P}_0\mathbf{y}.$$

Thus

$$\begin{aligned} (\boldsymbol{\phi}_0 - \boldsymbol{\phi}_1)'(\boldsymbol{\phi}_0 - \boldsymbol{\phi}_1) &= \mathbf{y}'(\mathbf{P}_0 - \mathbf{P}_1)\mathbf{y} \\ &= \mathbf{y}'\mathbf{P}_0\mathbf{C}'(\mathbf{C}\mathbf{P}_0\mathbf{C}')^{-1}\mathbf{C}\mathbf{P}_0\mathbf{y} \\ &= (\mathbf{C}\boldsymbol{\phi}_0)'(\mathbf{C}\mathbf{P}_0\mathbf{C}')^{-1}\mathbf{C}\boldsymbol{\phi}_0 \qquad (11.5.3) \\ &= \boldsymbol{\lambda}'(\mathbf{C}\mathbf{P}_0\mathbf{C}')\boldsymbol{\lambda}. \qquad (11.5.4) \end{aligned}$$

As σ^2 is unity the likelihood ratio is given by

$$L[H|G] = \frac{\exp\{-\tfrac{1}{2}\,\mathbf{y}(\mathbf{I}-\mathbf{P}_1)\,\mathbf{y}\}}{\exp\{-\tfrac{1}{2}\,\mathbf{y}(\mathbf{I}-\mathbf{P}_0)\,\mathbf{y}\}}$$

and therefore

$$-2\log L[H|G] = \mathbf{y}'(\mathbf{P}_0 - \mathbf{P}_1)\,\mathbf{y}. \tag{11.5.5}$$

For testing H we use the statistic $\mathbf{y}'(\mathbf{P}_0 - \mathbf{P}_1)\mathbf{y}$ which has a chi-squared distribution when H is true, and we reject H if this statistic is too large. From the above we see that this statistic can be expressed in the three forms (11.5.3)–(11.5.5), and each form defines a different test principle. Thus we accept H if $\mathbf{C}\boldsymbol{\phi}_0$ is "near enough" to zero (Wald principle), or if the Lagrange multiplier $\boldsymbol{\lambda}$ is "near enough" to zero (Lagrange multiplier principle), or if the likelihood ratio is "near enough" to unity.

If we put $\mathbf{C} = [\mathbf{A}'\mathbf{V}]_t$, $\Omega = E_n$, then $\mathbf{P}_0 = \mathbf{I}_n$ and equations (11.5.1) and (11.5.2) become

$$\mathbf{y} - \boldsymbol{\phi}_1 + [\mathbf{A}'\mathbf{V}]_t'\boldsymbol{\lambda} = \mathbf{0}$$

and

$$[\mathbf{A}'\mathbf{V}]_t\boldsymbol{\phi}_1 = \mathbf{0}$$

which are precisely the equations obtained in § 11.4 when $\boldsymbol{\lambda} = N^{\frac{1}{2}}\boldsymbol{\mu}$. Now using a Taylor expansion and (11.4.5),

$$\begin{aligned}[\mathbf{A}'\mathbf{V}]_t\boldsymbol{\phi}_0 &= [\mathbf{A}'\mathbf{V}]_t\,\mathbf{y} \\ &= N^{\frac{1}{2}}\mathbf{A}_t'(\boldsymbol{\theta}_0 - \boldsymbol{\theta}_*) \\ &= N^{\frac{1}{2}}\mathbf{a}(\boldsymbol{\theta}_0) + o_p(1),\end{aligned}$$

and by virtue of the remarks made after assumption (xiv)

$$[\mathbf{A}'\mathbf{B}^{-1}\mathbf{A}]_t = [\mathbf{A}'\mathbf{B}^{-1}\mathbf{A}]_0 + o_p(1),$$

where the inverse of the matrix on the right-hand side will exist for N sufficiently large. Combining these two results gives us

$$(\mathbf{C}\boldsymbol{\phi}_0)'(\mathbf{C}\mathbf{P}_0\mathbf{C}')^{-1}\mathbf{C}\boldsymbol{\phi}_0 = N\,\mathbf{a}'(\boldsymbol{\theta}_0)[\mathbf{A}'\mathbf{B}^{-1}\mathbf{A}]_0^{-1}\,\mathbf{a}(\boldsymbol{\theta}_0) + o_p(1),$$

the so-called Wald test statistic. From (11.4.1) and (11.3.6),

$$\begin{aligned}\mathbf{A}_t N^{\frac{1}{2}}\boldsymbol{\mu} &= \mathbf{A}_1 N^{\frac{1}{2}}\boldsymbol{\mu} + o_p(1) \\ &= -N^{\frac{1}{2}}\mathbf{D}N^{-1}\log L_N(\boldsymbol{\theta}_1) + o_p(1),\end{aligned}$$

and

$$\boldsymbol{\lambda}'\mathbf{C}\,\mathbf{P}_0\,\mathbf{C}'\boldsymbol{\lambda} = N[\mathbf{D}N^{-1}\log L_N(\boldsymbol{\theta}_1)]'\mathbf{B}_1^{-1}[\mathbf{D}N^{-1}\log L_N(\boldsymbol{\theta}_1)] + o_p(1),$$

the Lagrange multiplier test statistic.. Using a Taylor expansion and (11.3.1), we have

$$\log L_N(\boldsymbol{\theta}_1) - \log L_N(\boldsymbol{\theta}_0) = [\mathbf{D}\log L_N(\boldsymbol{\theta}_0)](\boldsymbol{\theta}_1 - \boldsymbol{\theta}_0) + \\ + \tfrac{1}{2}(\boldsymbol{\theta}_1 - \boldsymbol{\theta}_0)'[\mathbf{D}^2\log L_N(\boldsymbol{\theta}_0)](\boldsymbol{\theta}_1 - \boldsymbol{\theta}_0) + o_p(1), \\ = 0 - \tfrac{1}{2}N(\boldsymbol{\theta}_1 - \boldsymbol{\theta}_0)'\mathbf{B}_0(\boldsymbol{\theta}_1 - \boldsymbol{\theta}_0) + o_p(1)$$

and therefore, from (11.4.5),

$$\begin{aligned} -2\log[L_N(\boldsymbol{\theta}_1)/L_N(\boldsymbol{\theta}_0)] &= N(\boldsymbol{\theta}_1 - \boldsymbol{\theta}_0)'\mathbf{B}_0(\boldsymbol{\theta}_1 - \boldsymbol{\theta}_0) + o_p(1) \\ &= (\mathbf{y} - \boldsymbol{\phi}_1)'(\mathbf{y} - \boldsymbol{\phi}_1) + o_p(1) \\ &= \mathbf{y}'(\mathbf{I} - \mathbf{P}_1)\mathbf{y} + o_p(1) \\ &= \mathbf{y}'(\mathbf{P}_0 - \mathbf{P}_1)\mathbf{y} + o_p(1) \\ &= -2\log L[H \mid G] + o_p(1), \end{aligned}$$

the likelihood-ratio test statistic.

Thus the three statistics

$$N\,\mathbf{a}'(\boldsymbol{\theta}_0)[\mathbf{A}'\mathbf{B}^{-1}\mathbf{A}]_0\,\mathbf{a}(\boldsymbol{\theta}_0),$$

$$N^{-1}[\mathbf{D}\log L_N(\boldsymbol{\theta}_1)]'\mathbf{B}_1^{-1}[\mathbf{D}\log L_N(\boldsymbol{\theta}_1)],$$

and

$$-2\log[L_N(\boldsymbol{\theta}_1)/L_N(\boldsymbol{\theta}_0)]$$

are asymptotically distributed as χ_r^2 when H is true. When H is false but $\boldsymbol{\theta}_t$ is "near" W_1, then the above linear approximation is valid and the three statistics have an asymptotic non-central chi-squared distribution. When $\boldsymbol{\theta}_t$ is not "near" W_1, the linear approximation cannot be used and we can say nothing about the power of the tests except that it will tend to unity as N tends to infinity. This is obvious since, for example, $\sqrt{N}\,\mathbf{a}(\boldsymbol{\theta}_0)$ will be far from $\mathbf{0}$ when $\mathbf{a}(\boldsymbol{\theta}_0)$ is not near $\mathbf{0}$.

In order to calculate the maximum likelihood estimates $\boldsymbol{\theta}_0$ and $\boldsymbol{\theta}_1$ some iterative procedure is needed for solving the non-linear maximum likelihood equations. Details of this are given in Aitchison and Silvey (1960). A comparative discussion of the three test methods with examples is also given there and in Aitchison (1962).

APPENDIX 1

The following properties of positive definite matrices are used throughout the text. If $\mathbf{B}$ is an $n \times n$ positive definite matrix and $\mathbf{C}$ is an $n \times p$ matrix of rank p, then

Lemma 1. $\mathbf{B}$ can be expressed in the form $\mathbf{R}'\mathbf{R}$ where $\mathbf{R}$ is a non-singular $n \times n$ matrix, and

Lemma 2. $\mathbf{C}'\mathbf{B}\mathbf{C}$ is positive definite.

Proof. There exists an orthogonal matrix $\mathbf{T}$ such that $\mathbf{T}'\mathbf{B}\mathbf{T} = \text{diag}(\lambda_1, \ldots, \lambda_n)$ where the eigen values $\lambda_1, \ldots, \lambda_n$ of $\mathbf{B}$ are all positive. Let $\mathbf{S} = \text{diag}(\lambda_1^{-\frac{1}{2}}, \ldots, \lambda_n^{-\frac{1}{2}})$ and let $\mathbf{R} = (\mathbf{T}\mathbf{S})^{-1}$. Then $(\mathbf{T}\mathbf{S})'\mathbf{B}\mathbf{T}\mathbf{S} = \mathbf{I}_n$, $\mathbf{B} = \mathbf{R}'\mathbf{R}$ and lemma 1 is proved. Lemma 2 follows from the fact that $\mathbf{y}'\mathbf{C}'\mathbf{R}'\mathbf{R}\mathbf{C}\mathbf{y} = \mathbf{z}'\mathbf{z} \geqslant 0$, where $\mathbf{z} = \mathbf{R}\mathbf{C}\mathbf{y}$, and $\mathbf{z} = \mathbf{0}$ if and only if $\mathbf{y} = \mathbf{0}$ as $\mathbf{C}$ has full rank.

Lemma 3. Let $\mathbf{X}$ be an $n \times r$ matrix of rank p, and $\mathbf{H}$ a $t \times r$ matrix. Then the equations $\boldsymbol{\theta} = \mathbf{X}\boldsymbol{\beta}$, $\mathbf{0} = \mathbf{H}\boldsymbol{\beta}$ have a unique solution for $\boldsymbol{\beta}$ for every $\boldsymbol{\theta} \in R[\mathbf{X}]$ if and only if

(i) $R[\mathbf{X}'] \cap R[\mathbf{H}'] = \mathbf{0}$, and

(ii) the rank of $\mathbf{G}' = (\mathbf{X}', \mathbf{H}')$ is p.

Proof. We first of all find necessary and sufficient conditions for $\boldsymbol{\beta}$ to exist. Now $\boldsymbol{\beta}$ will exist if and only if

$$\boldsymbol{\phi} = \begin{bmatrix} \boldsymbol{\theta} \\ \mathbf{0} \end{bmatrix} \in R[\mathbf{G}] \text{ for every } \boldsymbol{\theta} \in R[\mathbf{X}].$$

This statement is equivalent to: every vector perpendicular to $R[\mathbf{G}]$ is perpendicular to $\boldsymbol{\phi}$ for every $\boldsymbol{\theta} \in R[\mathbf{X}]$. Let $\mathbf{y}' = (\mathbf{y}_X', \mathbf{y}_H')$ be any $t+n$ dimensional vector; then by lemma 1.2.1 we have the equivalent statements

$$\mathbf{G}'\mathbf{y} = \mathbf{0} \text{ implies that } \boldsymbol{\phi}'\mathbf{y} = 0;$$

or $$\mathbf{X}'\mathbf{y}_X + \mathbf{H}'\mathbf{y}_H = \mathbf{0} \text{ implies that } \boldsymbol{\theta}'\mathbf{y}_X = 0 \quad \text{for every } \boldsymbol{\theta} \in R[\mathbf{X}];$$

or $$\mathbf{X}'\mathbf{y}_X + \mathbf{H}'\mathbf{y}_H = \mathbf{0} \text{ implies that } \mathbf{X}'\mathbf{y}_X = \mathbf{0}$$

(and therefore $\mathbf{H}'\mathbf{y}_H = \mathbf{0}$ also). Thus $\boldsymbol{\beta}$ will exist if and only if no linear combination of the rows of $\mathbf{X}$ is a linear combination of the rows of $\mathbf{H}$ except $\mathbf{0}$, or $R[\mathbf{X}'] \cap R[\mathbf{H}'] = \mathbf{0}$.

If $\boldsymbol{\beta}$ is to be unique, then the columns of $\mathbf{G}$ must be linearly independent and therefore $\text{rank}[\mathbf{G}] = p$. This proof is from Scheffé (1959, p. 17).

Lemma 4. Let $\mathbf{A}_1, \mathbf{A}_2, \ldots, \mathbf{A}_m$ be a sequence of $n \times n$ matrices such that $\sum_i \mathbf{A}_i = \mathbf{I}_n$; then the following conditions are equivalent:

(i) $\sum_i r_i = n$, where $r_i = \text{rank}[\mathbf{A}_i]$;

(ii) $\mathbf{A}_i \mathbf{A}_j = \mathbf{0}$ for $i \neq j$; and

(iii) $\mathbf{A}_i^2 = \mathbf{A}_i$.

Proof. ((i) implies (ii) and (iii); this proof is due to Dr S. D. Silvey.)

Since
$$\mathbf{y} = \mathbf{I}_n \mathbf{y} = \mathbf{A}_1 \mathbf{y} + \mathbf{A}_2 \mathbf{y} + \ldots + \mathbf{A}_m \mathbf{y}, \tag{1}$$
(i) implies that $E_n = R[\mathbf{A}_1] \oplus \ldots \oplus R[\mathbf{A}_m]$.

Let $\mathbf{y} \in R[\mathbf{A}_j]$; then the unique expression of $\mathbf{y}$ in the above form is
$$\mathbf{y} = \mathbf{0} + \ldots + \mathbf{y} + \ldots + \mathbf{0}. \tag{2}$$
Since equations (1) and (2) must be equivalent as $\mathbf{y}$ has a unique decomposition, we have $\mathbf{A}_i \mathbf{y} = \mathbf{0}$ $(i \neq j)$ and $\mathbf{A}_j \mathbf{y} = \mathbf{y}$ when $\mathbf{y} \in R[\mathbf{A}_j]$. In particular, for *any* $\mathbf{x}$, we have by putting $\mathbf{y} = \mathbf{A}_j \mathbf{x}$, $\mathbf{A}_i \mathbf{A}_j \mathbf{x} = \mathbf{0}$ and $\mathbf{A}_j^2 \mathbf{x} = \mathbf{A}_j \mathbf{x}$. That is, $\mathbf{A}_i \mathbf{A}_j = \mathbf{0}$ for $i \neq j$ and $\mathbf{A}_j^2 = \mathbf{A}_j$, and (i) implies (ii) and (iii).

That (ii) implies (iii) is trivial; we simply multiply $\sum_j \mathbf{A}_j = \mathbf{I}_n$ by $\mathbf{A}_i$.

If (iii) is true and each $\mathbf{A}_i$ is idempotent, then $\text{rank}[\mathbf{A}_i] = \text{tr}[\mathbf{A}_i]$ (cf. §3.7). Thus
$$\begin{aligned} n &= \text{tr}[\mathbf{I}_n] \\ &= \text{tr}[\textstyle\sum_i \mathbf{A}_i] \\ &= \textstyle\sum_i \text{tr}[\mathbf{A}_i] \\ &= \textstyle\sum_i \text{rank}[\mathbf{A}_i] \\ &= \textstyle\sum_i r_i, \end{aligned}$$
and (iii) implies (i). This completes the proof of Lemma 4.

APPENDIX 2

The following results on matrix differentiation are used in Chapter 9. If $\partial/\partial \mathbf{M} = (\partial/\partial m_{ij})$, then

(a) $$\frac{\partial\,\mathrm{tr}[\mathbf{LMN}]}{\partial \mathbf{M}} = \mathbf{L}'\mathbf{N}'$$

(b) $$\frac{\partial\,\mathrm{tr}[\mathbf{M}'\mathbf{LMN}]}{\partial \mathbf{M}} = 2\mathbf{LMN} \qquad (\mathbf{L} \text{ and } \mathbf{N} \text{ symmetric})$$

(c) $$\frac{\partial \log|\mathbf{M}|}{\partial \mathbf{M}} = (\mathbf{M}')^{-1}.$$

The proofs of these relations are straightforward, and we illustrate the method by proving (a). Now

$$t = \mathrm{tr}[\mathbf{LMN}] = \sum_p \sum_r \sum_s l_{pr} m_{rs} n_{sp}.$$

Hence

$$\begin{aligned} \partial t/\partial m_{ij} &= \sum_p l_{pi} n_{jp} \\ &= \sum_p l'_{ip} n'_{pj} \\ &= (\mathbf{L}'\mathbf{N}')_{ij} \end{aligned}$$

and $$\partial t/\partial \mathbf{M} = \mathbf{L}'\mathbf{N}'.$$

Since $\mathrm{tr}[\mathbf{LMN}] = \mathrm{tr}[\mathbf{N}'\mathbf{M}'\mathbf{L}']$ and

$$\mathrm{tr}[(\mathbf{M}'\mathbf{L})(\mathbf{MN})] = \mathrm{tr}[(\mathbf{MN})(\mathbf{M}'\mathbf{L})]$$

we can deduce further relations

$$\frac{\partial\,\mathrm{tr}[\mathbf{LM}'\mathbf{N}]}{\partial \mathbf{M}} = \mathbf{NL}$$

and for $\mathbf{L}$, $\mathbf{N}$ symmetric

$$\frac{\partial\,\mathrm{tr}[\mathbf{MNM}'\mathbf{L}]}{\partial \mathbf{M}} = 2\mathbf{LMN}.$$

Checked out item summary for
COCKMAN, JOHN E
09-29-2006 4:11PM
BARCODE: 3050900708593 LOCATION: argen
TITLE: The linear hypothesis: a genera l
DUE DATE: 10-20-2006

REFERENCES

ABDEL-ATY, S.H. (1954). Approximate formulae for the percentage points and the probability integral of the non-central χ^2 distribution. *Biometrika,* **41**, 538-540.

AITCHISON, J. (1962). Large sample restricted parametric tests. *J. Roy. Statist. Soc., Series B,* **24**, 234-250.

AITCHISON, J. and SILVEY, S.D. (1960). Maximum likelihood estimation procedures and associated tests of significance. *J. Roy. Statist. Soc., Series B,* **22**, 154-171.

AITKEN, A.C. (1954). *Determinants and Matrices.* Oliver and Boyd: London.

ANDERSON, T.W. (1951). Estimating linear restrictions on regression coefficients for multivariate normal distributions. *Annals Math. Statist.,* **22**, 327-351.

ANDERSON, T.W. (1958). *An introduction to multivariate statistical analysis.* Wiley: New York.

ANDERSON, T.W. (1962). The choice of the degree of a polynomial regression as a multiple decision problem. *Annals Math. Statist.,* **33**, 255-265.

ANSCOMBE, F.J. (1960). Examination of residuals. *Proc. Fourth Berk. Symp. on Math. Stat. and Probability,* **1**, 1-36.

ATIQULLAH, M. (1962). The estimation of residual variance in quadratically balanced least squares problems and the robustness of the *F* test. *Biometrika,* **49**, 83-91.

ATIQULLAH, M. (1963). On the randomisation distribution and power of the variance ratio test. *J. Roy. Statist. Soc., Series B,* **25**, 334-347.

BARNARD, G.A. (1963). The logic of least squares. *J. Roy. Statist. Soc., Series B,* **25**, 111-115.

BARTLETT, M.S. (1937). Properties of sufficiency and statistical tests. *Proc. Roy. Soc. London, A,* **160**, 268-282.

BIGGERS, J.D. (1959). The estimation of missing and mixed-up observations in several experimental designs. *Biometrika,* **46**, 91-105.

BIRKHOFF, G. and MACLANE, S. (1953). *A survey of modern algebra.* Macmillan: New York.

BOX, G.E.P. and COX, D.R. (1964). An analysis of transformations. *J. Roy. Statist. Soc., Series B,* **26**, 211-252.

G.E.P. and TIAO, G.C. (1962). A further look at robustness ...yes' theorem. *Biometrika,* **49**, 419-432.

...P. and TIAO, G.C. (1964). A note on criterion robustness

and inference robustness. *Biometrika,* **51**, 169-173.

BOX, G. E. P. and WATSON, G. S. (1962). Robustness to non-normality of regression tests. *Biometrika,* **49**, 93-106.

CHAKRABARTI, M. C. (1962). *Mathematics of design and analysis of experiments.* Asia Publishing House: London.

CHIPMAN, J. S. (1964). On least squares with insufficient observations. *J. Amer. Stat. Assoc.,* **59**, 1078-1111.

COCHRAN, W. G. (1934). The distribution of quadratic forms in a normal system with applications to analysis of variance. *Proc. Camb. Phil. Soc.,* **30**, 178-191.

COCHRAN, W. G. (1938). The omission or addition of an independent variate in multiple linear regression. *Supp. J. Roy. Statist. Soc.,* **5**, 171-176.

COCHRAN, W. G. and COX, G. M. (1957). *Experimental designs* (2nd edn). Wiley: New York.

COLLIER, R. O., JR. and BAKER, F. B. (1963). The randomisation distribution of *F*-ratios for the split plot design–an empirical investigation. *Biometrika,* **50**, 431-438.

COONS, I. (1957). The analysis of covariance as a missing plot technique. *Biometrics,* **13**, 387-405.

COX, D. R. (1958). *Planning of experiments.* Wiley: New York.

DARROCH, J. N. and SILVEY, S. D. (1963). On testing more than one hypothesis. *Annals Math. Statist.,* **34**, 555-567.

DAVIES, O. L. (1956). *Design and analysis of industrial experiments.* Oliver and Boyd: London.

DRAPER, N. R. (1961). Missing values in response surface designs. *Technometrics,* **3**, 389-398.

DUNN, OLIVE J. (1959). Confidence intervals for the means of dependent, normally distributed variables. *J. Amer. Stat. Assoc.,* **54**, 613-621.

DURBIN, J. and KENDALL, M. G. (1951). The geometry of estimation. *Biometrika,* **38**, 150-158.

FAIRFIELD SMITH, H. (1957). Missing plot estimates. *Biometrics,* **13**, 115-118.

FEDERER, W. T. (1955). *Experimental design.* Macmillan: New York.

FERGUSON, T. S. (1960). On the rejection of outliers. *Proc. Fourth Berk. Symp. on Math. Stat. and Probability,* **1**, 253-287.

FINNEY, D. J. (1955). *Experimental design and its statistical basis.* Cambridge University Press: London.

FISHER, R. A. (1960). *Design of experiments* (6th edn). Oliver and Boyd: Edinburgh.

FREEMAN, G. H. and JEFFERS, J. N. R. (1962). Estimation of means and standard errors in the analysis of non-orthogonal experiments by electronic computers. *J. Roy. Statist. Soc., Series B,* **24**, 435-446.

GARSIDE, M. J. (1964). The best subset in multiple regression analysis. *Applied Statistics,* **13** (to appear).

GHOSH, M. N. (1963). Hotelling's generalised T^2 in the multivariate analysis of variance. *J. Roy. Statist. Soc., Series B,* **25**, 358-367.

GHOSH, M. N. and SHARMAN, D. (1963). Power of Tukey's test for additivity. *J. Roy. Statist. Soc., Series B,* **25**, 213-219.

GOOD, I. J. (1963). On the independence of quadratic expressions. *Annals Math. Statist.,* **25**, 377-382.

GRAYBILL, F. A. (1961). *An introduction to linear statistical models,* vol. I. McGraw-Hill: New York.

GRAYBILL, F. A. and MARSAGLIA, M. (1957). Idempotent matrices and quadratic forms in the general linear hypothesis. *Annals Math. Statist.,* **28**, 678-686.

HADLEY, G. (1961). *Linear Algebra.* Addison-Wesley: Reading, Massachusetts.

HALPERIN, M. (1963). Confidence interval estimation in non-linear regression. *J. Roy. Statist. Soc., Series B,* **25**, 330-333.

HALPERIN, M. (1964). Note on interval estimation in non-linear regression when responses are correlated. *J. Roy. Statist. Soc., Series B,* **26**, 267-269.

HICKS, C. R. (1964). *Fundamental concepts in the design of experiments.* Holt, Rinehart and Winston Inc: U.S.A.

HODGES, J. L. (1955). On the non-central beta-distribution. *Annals Math. Statist.,* **26**, 648-653.

HOGG, R. V. (1961). On the resolution of statistical hypotheses. *J. Amer. Stat. Assoc.,* **56**, 978-989.

HOGG, R. V. (1962). Iterated tests of the equality of several distributions. *J. Amer. Stat. Assoc.,* **57**, 579-585.

HOGG, R. V. and CRAIG, A. T. (1958). On the decomposition of certain variables. *Annals Math. Statist.,* **29**, 608-610.

HOTELLING, H. (1931). The generalisation of Student's ratio. *Annals Math. Statist.,* **2**, 360-378.

HOTELLING, H. (1951). A generalised T test and measure of multivariate dispersion. *Proc. Second Berk. Symp. on Math. Stat. and Probability,* **1**, 23-41.

HOTELLING, H. (1960). The behaviour of some standard statistical tests under non-standard conditions. *Proc. Fourth Berk. Symp. on Math. Stat. and Probability,* **1**, 319-360.

HSU, P. L. (1940). On generalised analysis of variance. *Biometrika,* **31**, 221-237.

HSU, P. L. (1941a). Analysis of variance from the power function standpoint. *Biometrika,* **32**, 62-69.

HSU, P.L. (1941b). Canonical reduction of the general regression problem. *Annals Eugen. London*, **11**, 42-46.

IMHOP, J.P. (1961). Computing the distribution of quadratic forms in normal variables. *Biometrika*, **48**, 419-426.

ITO, K. (1956). Asymptotic formula for the distribution of Hotelling's generalised T_0^2 statistic, I. *Annals Math. Statist.*, **27**, 1091-1105.

ITO, K. (1960). Asymptotic formula for the distribution of Hotelling's generalised T_0^2 statistic, II. *Annals Math. Statist.*, **31**, 1147-1153.

ITO, K. (1962). A comparison of powers of two multivariate analysis of variance tests. *Biometrika*, **49**, 455-462.

ITO, K. and SCHULL, W.J. (1964). On the robustness of the T_0^2 test in multivariate analysis of variance when variance-covariance matrices are not equal. *Biometrika*, **51**, 71-82.

JAMES, G.S. (1951). The comparison of several groups of observations when the ratios of the population variances are unknown. *Biometrika*, **38**, 324-329.

JAMES, G.S. (1954). Tests of linear hypotheses in univariate and multivariate analysis when the ratios of the population variances are unknown. *Biometrika*, **41**, 19-43.

JAMES, G.S. (1956). On the accuracy of weighted means and ratios. *Biometrika*, **43**, 304-321.

JOHN, P.W.M. (1964). Pseudo-inverses in the analysis of variance. *Annals Math. Statist.*, **35**, 895-896.

JOHNSON, N.L. (1959). On an extension of the connection between Poisson and χ^2 distributions. *Biometrika*, **46**, 352-353.

KABE, D.G. (1963). Multivariate linear hypotheses with linear restrictions. *J. Roy. Statist. Soc., Series B*, **25**, 348-351.

KEMPTHORNE, O. (1952). *The design and analysis of experiments.* Wiley: New York.

KENDALL, M.G. (1957). *Course in multivariate analysis.* Griffin: London.

KENDALL, M.G. and STUART, A. (1958). *The advanced theory of statistics:* Vol. 1, Distribution theory. Griffin: London.

KENDALL, M.G. and STUART, A. (1961). *The advanced theory of statistics:* Vol.2, Inference and relationship. Griffin: London.

KIEFER, J. (1958). On the non-randomised optimality and randomised non-optimality of symmetrical designs. *Annals Math. Statist.*, **29**, 675-699.

KRAMER, C.Y. (1955). On the analysis of variance of a two-way classification with unequal sub-class numbers. *Biometrics*, **11**, 441-452.

KRUSKAL, W. (1960). The coordinate free approach to Gauss-Markov estimation, and its application to missing and extra observations.

Proc. Fourth Berk. Symp. on Math. Stat. and Probability, **1**, 435-451.

LAWLEY, D.N. (1938). A generalisation of Fisher's Z test. *Biometrika*, **30**, 180-187.

LEHMANN, E.L. (1950). Some principles of the theory of testing hypotheses. *Annals Math. Statist.*, **1**, 1-26.

LEHMANN, E.L. (1959). *Testing statistical hypotheses.* Wiley: New York.

LEHMANN, E.L. (1964). Asymptotically non-parametric inference in some linear models with one observation per cell. *Annals Math. Statist.*, **35**, 726-734.

MANN, H.B. (1949). *Analysis and design of experiments.* Dover: New York.

MANN, H.B. and WALD, A. (1943). On stochastic limit and order relationships. *Annals Math. Statist.*, **14**, 217-226.

MITRA, S.K. (1960). On the F test in the intra-block analysis of a balanced incomplete block design. *Sankhyā*, **22**, 279-284.

MURDOCH, D.C. (1957). *Linear algebra for the undergraduate.* Wiley: New York.

NEYMAN, J. (1959). Optimal asymptotic tests of composite statistical hypotheses. *Probability and Statistics – The Harald Cramer Volume.* Almqvist and Wiksell.

OGAWA, J. (1963). On the null-distribution of the F-statistic in a randomised balanced incomplete block design under the Neyman model. *Annals Math. Statist.*, **34**, 1558-1567.

PATNAIK, P.B. (1949). The non-central χ^2 and F distributions and their applications. *Biometrika*, **36**, 202-232.

PEARCE, S.C. (1963). The use and classification of non-orthogonal designs. *J. Roy. Statist. Soc., Series A*, **126**, 353-377.

PEARSON, E.S. (1959). Note on the approximation to the distribution of non-central χ^2. *Biometrika*, **46**, 364.

PEARSON, E.S. and HARTLEY, H.O. (1956). *Biometrika tables for Statisticians*, Vol. 1. Cambridge University Press: London.

PILLAI, K.C.S. (1955). Some new test criteria in multivariate analysis. *Annals Math. Statist.*, **26**, 117-121.

PLACKETT, R.L. (1950). Some theorems in least squares. *Biometrika*, **37**, 149-157.

PLACKETT, R.L. (1960a). *Principles of regression analysis.* Clarendon Press: Oxford.

PLACKETT, R.L. (1960b). Models in the analysis of variance. *J. Roy. Statist. Soc., Series B*, **22**, 195-217.

PRICE, R. (1964). Some non-central F-distributions expressed in closed form. *Biometrika*, **51**, 107-122.

QUENOUILLE, M.H. (1948). The analysis of covariance and non-orthogonal comparisons. *Biometrics*, **4**, 240-246.

QUENOUILLE, M. H. (1950). An application of least squares to family diet surveys. *Econometrica*, **18**, 27-44.

QUENOUILLE, M. H. (1952). *Associated measurements*. Butterworth's Scientific Publications: London.

QUENOUILLE, M. H. (1953). *The design and analysis of experiment*. Griffin: London.

QUESENBERRY, C. P. and DAVID, H. A. (1961). Some tests for outliers. *Biometrika*, **48**, 379-387.

RALSTON, A. and WILF, H. S. (1960). *Mathematical methods for digital computers*. John Wiley: New York.

RAO, C. R. (1947). Large sample tests of statistical hypotheses concerning several parameters with applications to problems of estimation. *Proc. Camb. Phil. Soc.*, **44**, 50-57.

RAO, C. R. (1952a). Some theorems on minimum variance estimation. *Sankhyā*, **12**, 27-42.

RAO, C. R. (1952b). *Advanced statistical methods in biometric research*. Wiley: London.

RAO, C. R. (1959). Some problems involving linear hypotheses in multivariate analysis. *Biometrika*, **46**, 49-58.

RAO, C. R. (1962). A note on a generalised inverse of a matrix with applications to problems in mathematical statistics. *J. Roy. Statist. Soc., Series B*, **24**, 152-158.

ROY, S. N. (1957). *Some aspects of multivariate analysis*. Wiley: New York.

RUBEN, H. (1963). A new result on the distribution of quadratic forms. *Annals Math. Statist.*, **34**, 1582-1584.

SANKARAN, M. (1959). On the non-central χ^2 distribution. *Biometrika*, **36**, 235-237.

SAW, J. G. (1964). Some notes on variance-ratio tests of the general linear hypothesis. *Biometrika*, **51**, 511-518.

SCHEFFÉ, H. (1959). *The analysis of variance*. Wiley: New York.

SEBER, G. A. F. (1963). The non-central chi-squared and beta distributions. *Biometrika*, **50**, 542-544.

SEBER, G. A. F. (1964a). The linear hypothesis and idempotent matrices. *J. Roy. Statist. Soc., Series B*, **26**, 261-266.

SEBER, G. A. F. (1964b). Linear hypotheses and induced tests. *Biometrika*, **51**, 41-48.

SEBER, G. A. F. (1964c). The linear hypothesis and large sample theory. *Annals Math. Statist.*, **35**, 773-779.

SIDDIQUI, M. M. (1960). Tests for regression coefficients when errors are correlated. *Annals Math. Statist.*, **31**, 929-938.

SILVEY, S. D. (1959). The Lagrangian multiplier test. *Annals Math. Statist.*, **30**, 389-407.

SOLOMON, H. (1960). On the distribution of quadratic forms in normal variates. *Proc. Fourth Berk. Symp. on Math. Stat. and Probability*, **1**, 645-653.

SRIVASTAVA, J. N. (1964). On the monotonicity property of the three main tests for multivariate analysis of variance. *J. Roy. Statist. Soc., Series B*, **26**, 77-81.

STEVENS, W. L. (1961). Asymptotic regression. *Biometrics*, **7**, 247-267.

TANG, P. C. (1938). The power function of the analysis of variance test, with tables and illustrations of this use. *Statist. Res. Mem.*, **2**, 126-149.

THOMPSON, W. A. and WILLKE, T. A. (1963). On an extreme rank sum test for outliers. *Biometrika*, **50**, 375-383.

TIKU, M. L. (1964). Approximating the general non-normal variance-ratio sampling distributions. *Biometrika*, **51**, 83-95.

TOCHER, K. D. (1952). The design and analysis of block experiments. *J. Roy. Statist. Soc., Series B*, **14**, 45-91.

TRAWINSKI, I. M. and BARGMANN, R. E. (1964). Maximum likelihood estimation with incomplete multivariate data. *Annals Math. Statist.*, **35**, 647-657.

TUKEY, J. W. (1957). Approximations to the upper 5% point of Fisher's B distribution and non-central χ^2. *Biometrika*, **44**, 528-530.

TURNER, M. E., MONROE, R. J. and LUCAS, H. L. (1961). Generalised asymptotic regression and non-linear path analysis. *Biometrics*, **17**, 120-143.

WALD, A. (1942). On the power function of the analysis of variance test. *Annals Math. Statist.*, **13**, 434-439.

WALD, A. (1943). Tests of statistical hypotheses concerning several parameters when the number of observations is large. *Trans. Amer. Math. Soc.*, **54**, 426-482.

WALD, A. (1949). Note on the consistency of the maximum likelihood estimate. *Annals Math. Statist.*, **20**, 595-601.

WELCH, B. L. (1947). The generalisation of "Student's" problem when several different population variances are involved. *Biometrika*, **34**, 28-35.

WELCH, B. L. (1951). On the comparison of several mean values: an alternative approach. *Biometrika*, **38**, 330-336.

WILKINSON, G. N. (1957). The analysis of covariance with incomplete data. *Biometrics*, **13**, 363-372.

WILKINSON, G. N. (1958a). Estimation of missing values for the analysis of incomplete data. *Biometrics*, **14**, 257-286.

WILKINSON, G. N. (1958b). The analysis of variance of derivation of standard errors for incomplete data. *Biometrics*, **14**, 360-384.

WILKS, S. S. (1932). Certain generalisations in the analysis of variance. *Biometrika*, **24**, 471-494.

WILLIAMS, E. J. (1959). *Regression Analysis.* Wiley: New York.

WILLIAMS, E. J. (1962). Exact fiducial limits in non-linear estimation. *J. Roy. Statist. Soc., Series B*, **24**, 125-139.

WILSON, E. B. (1952). *Introduction to scientific research.* McGraw-Hill: New York.

WINER, B. J. (1962). *Statistical principles in experimental design.* McGraw-Hill: New York.

INDEX